PRENTICE HALL SCIENCE

Test Book

MOTION, FORCES, AND ENERGY

Prentice Hall
Englewood Cliffs, New Jersey
Needham, Massachusetts

Test Book

PRENTICE HALL SCIENCE
Motion, Forces, and Energy

ISBN 0-13-987918-8

8 9 10   96 95

Prentice Hall
A Division of Simon & Schuster
Englewood Cliffs, New Jersey 07632

Contents

To the Teacher

This *Test Book* contains all the testing materials that accompany the student textbook. The testing materials are divided into three parts:

CHAPTER TEST

Every chapter in the student textbook has an accompanying Chapter Test. These tests are meant to test both factual recall and concept development. Each Chapter Test is divided into five sections. These sections are Multiple Choice, Completion, True or False, Using Science Skills, and Essay. An Answer Key for each Chapter Test is also included.

COMPUTER TEST BANK TEST

Every chapter in the student textbook has an accompanying Computer Test Bank Chapter Test. These tests are meant to test both factual recall and concept development. Each Computer Test Bank Test is divided into five sections. These sections are Multiple Choice, True or False, Completion, Using Science Skills, and Critical Thinking and Application. An Answer Key for each Test Bank Test is also included.

You may choose to copy the entire Computer Test Bank Chapter Test. A complete User's Guide is included in the disk package. Using your computer and the test disks, you can print out your own chapter test, quiz, midterm, or final exam, selecting questions from the Test Bank as well as adding your own. An Illustration Master for each visual question in the Test Bank Test is included after the questions. These Illustration Masters are to be used when you print out a test from your printer. An Answer Key for each test is also included.

The APPLE, IBM, and MAC disks for the *Prentice Hall Science* Computer Test Banks include questions from the Computer Test Bank for all 19 titles in the program.

For current prices and ordering information call your Customer Service Representative toll free 1-800-848-9500. Refer to the appropriate ISBN number below.

Item (ISBN #)	Description
0-13-987686-3	Apple 5 1/4-inch Program and Data Disks for the *Prentice Hall Science* Computer Test Bank (User's Guide included)
0-13-987702-9	IBM 5 1/4-inch Program and Data Disks for the *Prentice Hall Science* Computer Test Bank (User's Guide included)
0-13-986944-1	IBM 3 1/2-inch Program and Data Disks for the *Prentice Hall Science* Computer Test Bank (User's Guide included)
0-13-987694-4	MAC 3 1/2-inch Program and Data Disks for the *Prentice Hall Science* Computer Test Bank (User's Guide included)

PERFORMANCE-BASED TESTS

A set of Performance-Based Tests is included in this *Test Book*. Performance-Based Tests are designed to test a student's thinking and problem-solving abilities and are not meant to be content dependent. Although the tests have been designed to be given when the student has completed the textbook, you may prefer to give individual tests after particular chapters in the textbook. If you like, you may incorporate some of the Performance-Based Tests into your Chapter Test.

Performance-Based Tests are given at workstations. All materials the student needs are placed at the workstation, along with the worksheets the student must fill out. Students must be told in advance the amount of time they will have at each workstation. Make sure students understand that they must leave the workstation exactly as they found it.

Contents

Chapter Test

CHAPTER 1 ■ What Is Motion?

MULTIPLE CHOICE

Write the letter of the correct answer on the line at the left.

_____ 1. Which of the following are important in measuring motion?
a. distance, time, speed
b. velocity, acceleration, density
c. distance, volume, speed
d. acceleration, momentum, speed

_____ 2. The distance traveled by an object per unit time is called
a. velocity.   c. momentum.
b. speed.   d. acceleration.

_____ 3. Motion is
a. an increase in the speed of an object.
b. a decrease in the speed of an object.
c. the stopping of an object relative to a frame of reference.
d. a change in position relative to a frame of reference.

_____ 4. Find the speed of an object that covers 400 km in 5 hr.
a. 40 km/hr   c. 2000 km/hr
b. 80 km/hr   d. 800 km/hr

_____ 5. Velocity is
a. the same as speed.
b. the same as acceleration.
c. speed in a specific direction.
d. the same as momentum.

_____ 6. Acceleration is the
a. rate of change in momentum.
b. rate of change in speed.
c. rate of change in velocity.
d. amount of time needed for an object to reach its destination.

_____ 7. Deceleration is
a. negative velocity.   c. negative acceleration.
b. negative speed.   d. negative density.

_____ 8. What is the acceleration of an object that takes 20 sec to change from a speed of 200 m/sec to 300 m/sec?
a. 5 m/sec   c. 100 m/sec
b. 5 m/sec/sec   d. 100 m/sec/sec

_____ **9.** An object traveling at a constant 20 m/sec in a circular path is changing its
  a. speed.   c. velocity.
  b. momentum.   d. mass.

_____ **10.** The object or point from which movement is determined is called
  a. terminal velocity.   c. momentum.
  b. motion.   d. frame of reference.

COMPLETION

Complete each statement on the line at the left.

_____ **1.** The most common frame of reference is the _____.

_____ **2.** The rate at which an object moves is called _____.

_____ **3.** The distance–time graph for constant speed is a(an) _____ line.

_____ **4.** The momentum of an object can be found by multiplying its mass times its _____.

_____ **5.** The length between two places is called _____.

TRUE OR FALSE

Determine whether each statement is true or false. If it is true, write T. If it is false, change the underlined word or words to make the statement true.

_____ _____ **1.** Movement can be measured only in reference to something that is assumed to be fixed in place.

_____ _____ **2.** Speed that does not change is called average speed.

_____ _____ **3.** Speed equals acceleration divided by time.

_____ _____ **4.** In circular motion, the velocity of an object is constantly changing.

_____ _____ **5.** The distance–time graph for acceleration is always a straight line.

Name _____ Class _____ Date _____

USING SCIENCE SKILLS: Interpreting a Diagram

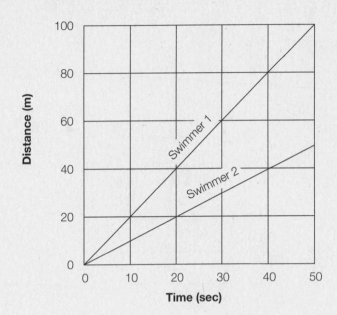

1. How many meters can Swimmer 1 cover in 30 sec? _____

2. How far will Swimmer 2 go in 30 sec? _____

3. Predict the number of m Swimmer 1 can go in 60 sec. _____

4. Predict the number of m Swimmer 2 can go in 60 sec. _____

5. Which swimmer has the greatest speed? _____

6. Calculate the speed of Swimmer 1. _____

7. Calculate the speed of Swimmer 2. _____

ESSAY

Write a brief paragraph discussing each of the following statements or questions.

1. In an amusement park you stand against the inside wall of a circular object that resembles a tin can. The circular object begins to whirl around. After a constant speed is reached, the floor drops down, but you are held fast against the whirling wall. Are you being accelerated? Explain your answer.

_____

_____

_____

_____

_____

Motion, Forces, and Energy   S ■ 11

2. A 500-kg car proceeding at a speed of 100 km/hr is in a head-on collision with a 1500-kg pickup truck going 10 km/hr. The smaller car pushes the pickup truck back. Explain this situation.

_____

_____

_____

_____

_____

3. You are riding on a train going north and you see a car traveling north parallel to the train. Yet the car seems to be going backward. Explain this occurrence.

_____

_____

_____

_____

_____

4. Explain why the pilot of a plane must have precise measurements of velocity.

_____

_____

_____

_____

_____

5. Explain why the slowing down of a moving object is considered to be a form of acceleration.

_____

_____

_____

_____

_____

Answer Key

MULTIPLE CHOICE

1. a **2.** b **3.** d **4.** b **5.** c **6.** c **7.** c **8.** b **9.** c **10.** d

COMPLETION

1. Earth **2.** speed **3.** straight **4.** velocity **5.** distance

TRUE OR FALSE

1. T **2.** F, constant **3.** F, distance **4.** T **5.** F, curved

USING SCIENCE SKILLS

1. 60 **2.** 30 **3.** 120 **4.** 60 **5.** swimmer 1 **6.** 2 m/sec **7.** 1 m/sec

ESSAY

1. Yes. Acceleration is the rate of change in velocity. Velocity is changing, even though speed is remaining constant, because velocity is a change in direction as well as a change in speed.
2. Momentum is mass multiplied by velocity. The momentum of the small car is 500 kg times 100 km/hr, which equal 50,000 kg-km/hr. The momentum of the truck is 1500 kg times 10 km/hr, which equals 15,000 kg-km/hr. The momentum of the car is greater. **3.** The train is traveling faster than the car. Your frame of reference is inside the faster moving train. The car is seen to be moving backward by an observer in the train, although a third observer on the ground would see both as moving in the same direction. **4.** A measure of velocity, which consists of both a speed measurement and a direction measurement, is necessary so that a pilot can guide the plane to its correct destination. **5.** Acceleration is defined as a change in the velocity of an object. Since an object that is slowing down is changing its speed, thus velocity, it is accelerating.

Test Bank Test

CHAPTER 1 ■ What Is Motion?

MULTIPLE CHOICE

Write the letter of the answer that best completes each statement.

_____ **1.** Our most common frame of reference is the
    a. Earth.   c. moon.
    b. sun.   d. atmosphere.

_____ **2.** Motion is measured by
    a. distance.   c. time.
    b. distance and direction.   d. time and distance.

_____ **3.** Motion can be measured in
    a. meters.   c. seconds per meter.
    b. kilometers.   d. meters per second.

_____ **4.** The length between two places is
    a. motion.   c. time.
    b. distance.   d. speed.

_____ **5.** How fast must a 100-kg object be going in order for it to stop a 200-kg object moving at 10 km/hr when the two objects collide head-on?
    a. 20 km/hr   c. 2 km/hr
    b. 200 km/hr   d. 1000 km/hr

_____ **6.** If a runner travels 50 m in 5 sec, his average speed is
    a. 50 m/sec.   c. 10 sec/m.
    b. 5 sec/m.   d. 10 m/sec.

_____ **7.** To calculate velocity, you need to know the total
    a. distance of the motion.
    b. time of the motion.
    c. distance and time of the motion.
    d. distance, time, and direction of the motion.

_____ **8.** To determine speed, you need to know the total
    a. distance of the motion.   c. distance and time of the motion.
    b. time of the motion.   d. distance, time, and direction of the motion.

_____ **9.** An object rolls toward the east at a steady speed of 12 m/sec for 3 sec. What distance does it travel?
    a. 7 m   c. 24 m
    b. 63 m   d. 18 m

_____ **10.** The rate of change in velocity is called
    a. acceleration.   c. average velocity.
    b. distance.   d. constant speed.

_____ **11.** The velocity of an object changes if
     a. its speed changes.
     b. its direction changes.
     c. either its speed or its direction changes.
     d. neither its speed nor its direction changes.

_____ **12.** A unit of length divided by a unit of time describes
     a. speed.   c. acceleration.
     b. velocity.   d. momentum.

_____ **13.** In one-half hour, a car traveled 20 km. Its average speed was
     a. 60 km.   c. 40 km.
     b. 10 km/hr.   d. 40 km/hr.

_____ **14.** If you row a boat upstream at 10 km/hr and the river has a downstream velocity of 5 km/hr, you are actually moving at
     a. 5 km/hr downstream.   c. 10 km/hr upstream.
     b. 15 km/hr downstream.   d. 5 km/hr upstream.

_____ **15.** Acceleration can be calculated by
     a. measuring speed and time.
     b. dividing distance by time.
     c. dividing the change in velocity by the time needed for that change.
     d. dividing the time needed for a change in velocity by that change in velocity.

_____ **16.** Subtracting original velocity from final velocity, or final velocity from original velocity, produces the value for
     a. acceleration.
     b. change in velocity
     c. average velocity.
     d. change in acceleration.

_____ **17.** When deceleration occurs, velocity
     a. has decreased.   c. is unchanging.
     b. has increased.   d. has reached zero.

_____ **18.** An automobile travels 30 m from its starting point in 5 sec. Its average speed is
     a. 6 m/sec.   c. 35 m/sec.
     b. 30 m/sec.   d. 150 m/sec.

_____ **19.** The value for average speed can be found by
     a. adding the total distance and the total time involved.
     b. dividing two distances by two.
     c. dividing distance covered by an instant of time.
     d. dividing the total distance by the total time involved.

_____ **20.** An example of constantly changing velocity is
     a. average velocity.
     b. constant speed.
     c. circular motion.
     d. a horizontal line on a distance–time graph.

_____ **21.** Even when moving slowly, an ocean liner cannot stop suddenly because of its
     a. large acceleration.   c. small acceleration.
     b. large momentum.   d. small momentum.

_____ **22.** The product of the mass of a moving object times its velocity is its
    a. speed.
    b. slope.
    c. acceleration.
    d. momentum.

_____ **23.** Movement can be measured only with reference to something that
    a. is assumed to be fixed in place.
    b. moves in the same direction.
    c. moves in the opposite direction.
    d. moves with inconsistent speed.

_____ **24.** Speed that does not change is called
    a. velocity.
    b. terminal velocity.
    c. constant speed.
    d. average speed.

_____ **25.** Acceleration can be measured in
    a. m/sec.
    b. sec.
    c. m/sec/sec.
    d. m.

_____ **26.** Negative acceleration is the same as
    a. terminal velocity.
    b. an increase in speed.
    c. an increase in velocity.
    d. deceleration.

_____ **27.** Which of the following is accelerating?
    a. a car traveling 33 km/hr slows to 25 km/hr
    b. a car traveling 33 km/hr speeds up to 42 km/hr
    c. a car traveling 35 km/hr due north turns east while still traveling 33 km/hr
    d. all of these

_____ **28.** The Law of Conservation of Momentum states that
    a. momentum can be gained but not lost.
    b. momentum can be lost but not gained.
    c. momentum cannot be lost or gained.
    d. momentum eventually turns into heat energy.

_____ **29.** A distance–time graph for acceleration is always a
    a. straight line.
    b. crooked line.
    c. curved line.
    d. wavy line.

_____ **30.** When an object slows,
    a. its velocity changes.
    b. its speed changes.
    c. its momentum changes.
    d. all of the above changes take place.

TRUE OR FALSE

Determine whether each statement is true or false

_____ **31.** There is always one correct frame of reference in a given situation.

_____ **32.** Motion must be measured relative to a frame of reference.

_____ **33.** Average speed always means that speed is constant.

_____ **34.** Dividing the total distance by the total time at any instant of time always gives the actual speed at that instant of time.

_____ **35.** Speed is acceleration in a certain direction.

_____ **36.** Acceleration and deceleration occur with change in velocity.

_____ **37.** A unit for momentum is kg-m/sec.

_____ **38.** A distance–time graph for constant speed is always a curve.

_____ **39.** Circular motion has constant velocity.

_____ **40.** An example of a velocity is 40 km/hr.

COMPLETION

Fill in the word or number that best completes each statement.

_____ **41.** The distance traveled by a moving object per unit of time is called _____.

_____ **42.** Unchanged speed is referred to as _____ speed.

_____ **43.** The statement that a hurricane is moving at 20 km/hr in an easterly direction is a description of the hurricane's _____.

_____ **44.** The motion of a car moving from a speed of 10 m/sec to 30 m/sec is called _____.

_____ **45.** A runner who runs 10 m in 1 sec and 20 m in 2 sec is running at a speed that is described as being _____.

_____ **46.** Dividing total distance by total time gives the kind of speed called _____.

_____ **47.** Velocities that have the same direction combine by the process of _____.

_____ **48.** Acceleration is the rate of change in _____.

_____ **49.** According to the Law of Conservation of Momentum, when one of two objects in a group loses momentum, the other object _____ momentum.

_____ **50.** Deceleration is called _____ acceleration.

_____ **51.** Mass times velocity equals _____.

_____ **52.** The stopping distance of a car is directly related to the concept called _____.

_____ **53.** A change in an object's position in a certain amount of time is called _____.

_____ **54.** The rate at which an object moves is called _____.

_____ 55. Speed in a given direction is called _____.

_____ 56. The background or object that is used to describe an object's movement is called the _____.

_____ 57. The length between two places is called _____.

_____ 58. If something is _____, it is speeding up, slowing down, or changing direction.

_____ 59. A distance–time graph for acceleration is a(an) _____ line.

_____ 60. In _____ motion, the velocity is continuously changing because direction is continuously changing.

USING SCIENCE SKILLS

Use the skills you have developed in the chapter to answer each question.

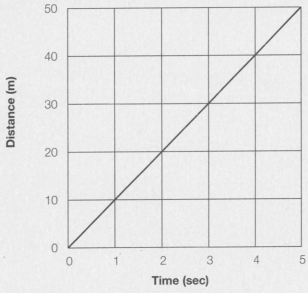

Figure 1

61. What type of graph is shown in Figure 1?

62. What does the line on the graph in Figure 1 represent?

63. According to Figure 1, what kind of motion is being described? What does such motion mean?

64. What unit of speed is represented in Figure 1?

65. According to Figure 1, what distance was covered in 3.5 sec?

66. According to Figure 1, did the object start from rest? Explain your answer.

67. According to Figure 1, what was the average speed of the object?

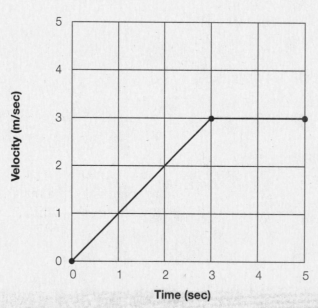

Figure 2

68. What type of graph is shown in Figure 2?

69. What does the line segment on the graph in Figure 2 from 0 to 3 sec represent? Explain your answer.

70. According to Figure 2, how did the velocity change from 0 to 3 sec?

71. What happened to the velocity in the final 2 sec shown in the graph in Figure 2?

72. Is there evidence of deceleration in any part of the graph in Figure 2? Explain your answer.

73. According to the graph in Figure 2, did the object change position in the final 2 sec? Explain your answer.

CRITICAL THINKING AND APPLICATION

Discuss each of the following in a brief paragraph.

74. Explain why rain falling to the Earth appears to the driver of a moving automobile to be moving somewhat horizontally (sideways) toward the windshield of the car.

75. Explain how to find the average speed of a car that travels 300 km in 6 hr. Solve for the speed.

76. You are in a boat on a river going downstream. The speedometer on the boat shows 50 km/hr. However, the boat is actually going faster than this. How is this possible?

77. Describe the difference between acceleration and deceleration.

78. People living at the Earth's equator are traveling at a speed of about 1670 km/hr as the Earth spins on its axis. Explain why these people do not feel themselves moving at this rapid speed.

79. You are riding in a car traveling 80 km/hr. A fly trapped in the car rests on your shoulder. Describe the speed of the fly using two different frames of reference.

80. Draw and label a distance–time graph of the motion of an object traveling at a constant speed of 2 m/sec for 3 sec.

81. Draw and label a velocity–time graph for a mass that travels north at a constant speed of 30 km/hr for 3 hr, then goes to zero km/hr for the next 2 hr, and finally accelerates uniformly to 50 km/hr within the next hr.

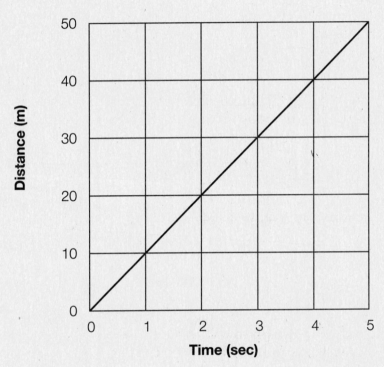

Figure 1

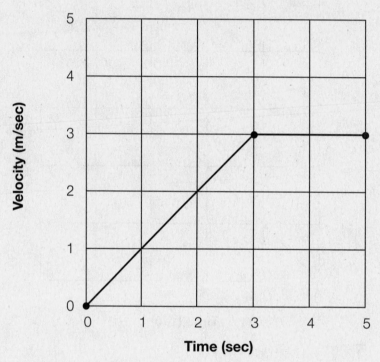

Figure 2

Test Bank Answer Key

1. a	15. c	29. c
2. d	16. b	30. d
3. d	17. a	31. F
4. b	18. a	32. T
5. a	19. d	33. F
6. d	20. c	34. F
7. d	21. b	35. F
8. c	22. d	36. T
9. b	23. a	37. T
10. a	24. c.	38. F
11. c	25. c	39. F
12. a	26. d	40. F
13. d	27. d	
14. d	28. c	

41. speed
42. constant
43. velocity
44. acceleration
45. constant
46. average speed
47. addition
48. velocity
49. gains
50. negative
51. momentum
52. momentum
53. motion
54. speed
55. velocity
56. frame of reference
57. distance
58. accelerating
59. curved
60. circular
61. distance–time graph
62. speed
63. Constant or uniform motion, which means the same amount of distance is covered per unit of time.
64. meters/second
65. 35 m
66. Yes. Both distance and time were at zero, the point of origin on the graph.
67. 10 m/sec
68. acceleration, or velocity–time graph
69. Constant acceleration. The uniform change in velocity per unit time produces a straight line.
70. The velocity went from 0 to 3 m/sec, or a gain of 1 m/sec/sec.
71. The velocity was unchanging; it remained at 3 m/sec.
72. No. Negative acceleration is a decrease in velocity, and according to the graph, velocity first increased to 3 m/sec (in the first 3 sec) and then remained constant at 3 m/sec for the last 2 sec.

73. Yes. Since distance = velocity × time, distance = 3 m/sec × 2 sec = 6 m. The object moved 6 m.

74. Motion is described according to a frame of reference. For the driver, whose frame of reference is a moving car, the rain seems to be coming horizontally toward her as she drives into it. Standing motionlessly on the ground, an observer sees rain falling vertically, with the Earth as a frame of reference.

75. Speed = distance/time; speed = 300 km/6 hr; speed = 50 km/hr.

76. The river is also moving. Since you are going downstream, the velocity of the river is added to the velocity of the boat. The velocity of the boat plus the velocity of the river is the velocity at which you are traveling.

77. The rate of change in velocity is called acceleration. An object accelerates if it speeds up, slows down, or changes direction. Deceleration is negative acceleration which occurs when a moving object slows down.

78. People use the objects around them as frames of reference by which they measure motion. Since all of the objects on the Earth are traveling at about 1670 km/hr at the equator, they remain stationary in relation to each other, and the Earth's rapid motion remains undetected.

79. If you use the Earth as a frame of reference, the fly is traveling at a speed of 80 km/hr, since it is inside the moving car. If you use yourself as a frame of reference, the fly is traveling at a speed of 0 km/hr, since it is resting on your shoulder and not moving in relation to you.

80.

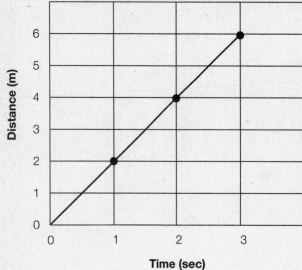

81.

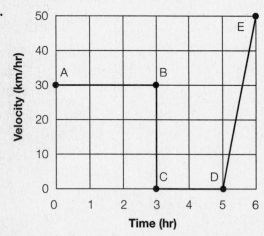

Straight line from A to B indicates constant velocity of 30 km/hr for the first 3 hr. From the third to the fifth hour, line from C to D indicates passage of time, but no motion. D to E indicates acceleration from 0 km/hr to 50 km/hr in the fifth to sixth hour.

Contents

CHAPTER 2

Chapter Test

CHAPTER 2 ■ The Nature of Forces

MULTIPLE CHOICE

Write the letter of the correct answer on the line at the left.

_____ **1.** No force is necessary to
   a. start an object moving.
   b. stop an object from moving.
   c. cause a change in the motion of an object.
   d. keep an object doing what it is already doing.

_____ **2.** The amount of sliding friction depends on the
   a. weight of the moving object and the type of surface that the
      object slides across.
   b. density and volume of the object.
   c. acceleration and mass of the object.
   d. density and mass of the object.

_____ **3.** Which of the following is *not* used to reduce friction?
   a. wheels   c. oil
   b. ball bearings   d. rough surfaces

_____ **4.** Which of the following is *not* a fluid?
   a. air   c. water
   b. sugar   d. oil

_____ **5.** When forces are balanced, the motion of the object
   a. is decreased.
   b. is increased.
   c. does not change.
   d. is completely stopped.

_____ **6.** For every action, the reaction is
   a. equal and in the same direction.
   b. equal and opposite.
   c. unequal and opposite.
   d. unequal and in the same direction.

_____ **7.** Near the surface of the Earth, the acceleration due to gravity is 9.8 m/sec/sec.
   After falling 6 sec, an object would have a velocity of
   a. 3.8 m/sec.   c. 15.8 m/sec.
   b. 9.8 m/sec.   d. 58.8 m/sec.

_____ **8.** Motion when an unbalanced force acts on an object is described by Newton's
   a. first law of motion.
   b. second law of motion.
   c. third law of motion.
   d. law of universal gravitation.

_____ 9. The weight of an object varies with the
   a. pull of gravity.
   b. volume of the object.
   c. dimensions of the object.
   d. speed of the object.

_____ 10. Newton's third law of motion describes
   a. motion when a balanced force acts on an object.
   b. motion when an unbalanced force acts on an object.
   c. why forces act in pairs.
   d. all aspects of an object's motion.

COMPLETION

Complete each statement on the line at the left.

_____ 1. A _____ is a push or pull that give energy to an object, causing that object to start moving, stop moving, or change its motion.

_____ 2. The force that opposes motion is _____.

_____ 3. Forces that are opposite and equal are called _____ forces.

_____ 4. Unbalanced forces always cause a _____ in motion.

_____ 5. _____ is the tendency of matter to resist any change in motion.

TRUE OR FALSE

Determine whether each statement is true or false. If it is true, write T. If it is false, change the underlined word or words to make the statement true.

_____ _____ 1. Isaac Newton developed three laws that describe all states of motion.

_____ _____ 2. Force equals mass times inertia.

_____ _____ 3. The friction produced by wheels or ball bearings is called sliding friction.

_____ _____ 4. The size of the force of gravity between two objects depends on the volume of the two objects and the distance between them.

_____ _____ 5. Weight is measured in newtons.

USING SCIENCE SKILLS: Interpreting Diagrams

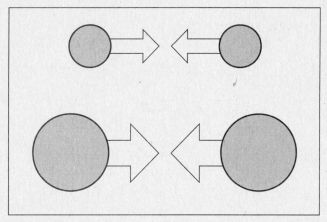

Figure A

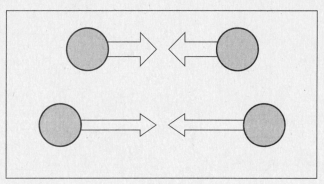

Figure B

1. Compare the size of the gravitational attraction between the top objects in Figure A to the size of the gravitational attraction between the bottom objects in Figure A.

_____

_____

2. What causes this difference?

_____

_____

3. Compare the size of the gravitational attraction between the top objects in Figure B to the size of the gravitational attraction between the bottom objects in Figure B.

_____

_____

4. What causes this difference?

_____

_____

5. Are all of these forces balanced or unbalanced? Explain your answer.

_____

_____

ESSAY

Write a brief paragraph discussing each of the following statements or questions.

1. Compare the three types of friction.

_____

_____

_____

_____

_____

_____

2. Compare the effect of a balanced force with that of an unbalanced force.

_____

_____

_____

_____

_____

_____

3. Explain the relationship between the force of gravity and the mass of the two objects and the distance between them.

_____

_____

_____

_____

_____

_____

4. Why does a person weigh less on the moon than on the Earth?

_____

_____

_____

_____

_____

_____

_____

5. Use Newton's first and second laws to explain why the seat-belt law saves lives.

_____

_____

_____

_____

_____

_____

_____

Answer Key

MULTIPLE CHOICE

1. d 2. a 3. d 4. b 5. c 6. b 7. d 8. b 9. a 10. c

COMPLETION

1. force 2. friction 3. balanced 4. change 5. Inertia

TRUE OR FALSE

1. T 2. F, acceleration 3. F, rolling 4. F, mass 5. T

USING SCIENCE SKILLS

1. Gravitational attraction between the top two objects in Figure A is less than between the objects below them. 2. The top objects in Figure A have less mass. 3. Gravitational attraction between the top two objects in Figure B is greater than the objects below them. 4. The top two objects in Figure B are closer together. 5. Because these forces are opposite and equal, they are balanced forces.

ESSAY

1. Sliding friction occurs when two solid surfaces slide over each other. The rougher the surface, the greater the friction will be. Rolling friction is produced when an object rolls over a surface. Rolling friction usually produces less friction than sliding friction. Fluid friction is produced when an object moves through a fluid. Fluid friction usually produces less friction than either sliding or rolling friction. 2. A balanced force does not produce any change in the motion of an object. An unbalanced force can cause motion or a change in motion. Balanced forces are equal and opposite. When two forces are unbalanced, one force is greater than the other. 3. The size of the force of gravity varies directly with mass and inversely with distance. Objects having a small mass have a small gravitational attraction for other objects. Objects having a large mass have a large gravitational attraction for other objects. The gravitational attraction of the Earth for the moon holds the moon in orbit. If the distance between them were greater, the Earth could not exert enough force to hold the moon in orbit. 4. The mass of the moon is less than the mass of the Earth, so its gravitational force is less. Since weight is a measure of the force of gravity, the object weighs less on the moon. 5. Inertia is the tendency of an object to resist any change in its motion. A passenger in a car that is traveling in a straight line is traveling at the same speed as the car. An unbalanced force is applied to the car, causing it to stop. If no unbalanced force, such as that provided by a seat belt, is applied to the passenger, he or she will keep moving in a straight line right through the windshield.

Test Bank Test

CHAPTER 2 ■ The Nature of Forces

MULTIPLE CHOICE

Write the letter of the answer that best completes each statement.

_____ **1.** Forces can cause objects to
   a. stop moving only.
   b. change direction only.
   c. start moving only.
   d. start moving, change direction, or stop moving.

_____ **2.** A force that sets an object into motion is
   a. balanced.   c. unbalanced.
   b. friction.   d. inertia.

_____ **3.** The direction of the frictional force on a moving object is
   a. opposite to the motion of the moving object.
   b. the same as the motion of the moving object.
   c. not going to alter the acceleration of the moving object.
   d. never responsible for stopping the motion of that object.

_____ **4.** Wheels and ball bearings change sliding friction to
   a. static friction.   c. fluid friction.
   b. rolling friction.   d. all types of friction.

_____ **5.** The function of lubricants is to change
   a. fluid friction to sliding friction.
   b. fluid friction to rolling friction.
   c. sliding friction to fluid friction.
   d. sliding friction to rolling friction.

_____ **6.** Treads on tires
   a. increase friction.   c. decrease stopping motion.
   b. reduce friction.   d. prevent the braking of a car.

_____ **7.** An example of rolling friction is
   a. a stack of cartons being pushed across a floor.
   b. the use of ball bearings.
   c. the fall of a feather through the air.
   d. sand placed on an icy walk.

_____ **8.** An example of friction other than sliding or rolling is
   a. pushing a desk across a floor.
   b. walking across a floor.
   c. floating downward after diving off a cliff.
   d. riding on a skateboard.

_____ 9. An example of balanced forces is
    a. a person skating back and forth on a rink.
    b. a tire with treads gaining speed on an icy road.
    c. two soccer players running in opposite directions.
    d. a book resting on a desk.

_____ 10. The sum of balanced forces equals
    a. zero.   c. two.
    b. one.   d. three.

_____ 11. The head of the arrow representing a force indicates the
    a. size of the force.   c. direction of the force.
    b. strength of the force.   d. sum of the forces.

_____ 12. When a car moves at constant velocity, the
    a. wheels are balanced.
    b. frictional force is greater than the engine's force.
    c. engine's force is greater than the frictional force.
    d. engine's force is equal to the frictional force.

_____ 13. A standoff in an arm-wrestling match is due to
    a. sliding frictional forces.   c. fluid frictional forces.
    b. rolling frictional forces   d. balanced forces.

_____ 14. Forces that are not opposite and equal are
    a. sliding.   c. balanced.
    b. rolling.   d. unbalanced.

_____ 15. Balanced forces cause
    a. a moving particle to slow down.   c. no change in motion.
    b. a moving particle to speed up.   d. a change in direction.

_____ 16. The combination of two forces exerted in opposite directions is the
    a. sum of the two forces.
    b. difference between the two forces.
    c. product of the two forces.
    d. ratio of the two forces.

_____ 17. If there is an unbalanced force in an arm-wrestling match,
    a. both arms will move in the direction of the smaller force.
    b. both arms will move in the direction of the larger force.
    c. the arms will move in opposite directions.
    d. the arms will be stationary.

_____ 18. When two forces acting in the same direction are applied to a mass, the combined force is the
    a. sum of the two forces.
    b. difference between the two forces.
    c. product of the two forces.
    d. ratio of the two forces.

_____ 19. The first law of motion states
    a. that an object at rest will remain at rest.
    b. that an object in motion will remain in motion at constant velocity.
    c. that an unbalanced force can change the velocity of an object in motion.
    d. all of the above.

_____ **20.** The law of motion that describes action-reaction is the
    a. first law.   c. third law.
    b. second law.   d. law of gravity.

_____ **21.** One newton equals one
    a. kg.   c. kg-m/sec.
    b. kg-m.   d. kg-m/sec/sec.

_____ **22.** Why forces act in pairs is explained by Newton's
    a. first law of motion.   c. third law of motion.
    b. second law of motion.   d. law of acceleration.

_____ **23.** A book resting on a desk
    a. has unbalanced forces acting on it.
    b. has weight due to gravitational force.
    c. exerts no force.
    d. has weight but not mass.

_____ **24.** Gravitational force between two objects depends on the
    a. masses of the objects and the distance between them.
    b. mass of each object only.
    c. distance between the objects only.
    d. inertia and masses of the objects.

_____ **25.** Gravity keeps
    a. only the Earth in its orbit.
    b. only the moon in its orbit around the Earth.
    c. only the Earth, Venus, and Mars in the solar system.
    d. the entire solar system together.

_____ **26.** A mass of 5 kg has a weight of
    a. 5 kg m/sec/sec.   c. 49 kg m/sec.
    b. 5 N.   d. 49 N.

_____ **27.** If you were on the moon, there would be a change in your
    a. weight and mass.   c. mass.
    b. weight.   d. volume.

_____ **28.** The attractive force between all objects in the universe is called
    a. inertia.   c. magnetism.
    b. gravity.   d. a push or a pull.

_____ **29.** A force
    a. is a push or a pull.   c. can cause an object to change its motion.
    b. gives energy to an object. d. can do all of the above

_____ **30.** An example of fluid friction is
    a. rolling friction.
    b. sliding friction.
    c. air resistance.
    d. produced when two rough surfaces slide against each other.

TRUE OR FALSE

Determine whether each statement is true or false.

_____ **31.** Forces change the speed of objects by changing the amount of energy the objects have.

_____ **32.** Fluid friction opposes motion to a greater degree than sliding friction does.

_____ **33.** Balanced forces are always equal and in the same direction.

_____ **34.** Balanced forces maintain motion at a constant velocity.

_____ **35.** The property of matter that resists any change in motion is called weight.

_____ **36.** An unbalanced force changes the velocity of an object.

_____ **37.** On the Earth's surface, the force of gravity increases as the masses of objects increase.

_____ **38.** According to Newton's second law of motion, force equals mass times weight.

_____ **39.** The force of gravity increases as the masses of objects decrease.

_____ **40.** Weight is measured in units called newtons.

COMPLETION

Fill in the word or number that best completes each statement.

_____ **41.** A push or pull is called a(an) _____.

_____ **42.** Near the surface of the Earth, the numerical value for the acceleration due to gravity is _____.

_____ **43.** Three types of friction are sliding, rolling, and _____.

_____ **44.** The type of friction that presents the greatest opposition to motion is _____ friction.

_____ **45.** The kind of friction experienced by a bird in flight is _____ friction.

_____ **46.** Forces that are equal in size and opposite in direction are described as _____ forces.

_____ **47.** Forces that always cause changes in motion are described as _____ forces.

_____ **48.** The laws of motion were developed by the scientist _____.

_____ **49.** An object in motion would continue to move forever if it were not for the presence of _____.

_____ **50.** A moving object's motion is opposed by the force called _____.

_____ **51.** Newton's first law of motion deals with the property of matter that resists a change in motion, or _____.

_____ **52.** When an object accelerates in the direction of the force acting upon it, that force is described as _____.

_____ **53.** The unit commonly used to measure force is the _____.

_____ **54.** Acceleration is determined by the force acting on an object and by that object's _____.

_____ **55.** According to the third law of motion, all forces come in _____.

_____ **56.** Mass times acceleration due to gravity equals the force called _____.

_____ **57.** A body in motion tends to stay in motion due to its _____.

_____ **58.** Newton's law of universal gravitation states that all objects in the universe attract each other by the force of _____.

_____ **59.** _____ equals mass times acceleration.

_____ **60.** As the distance between two objects decreases, the force of gravity between the objects _____.

USING SCIENCE SKILLS

Use the skills you have developed in the chapter to answer each question.

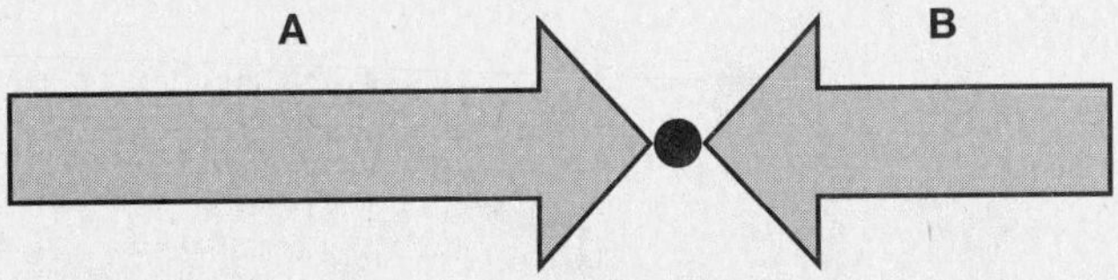

Figure 3

61. According to Figure 3, what is represented by the two arrows and the dot between them?

62. Do the arrows in Figure 3 show a balanced condition? Explain your answer.

63. What do the heads of the arrows in Figure 3 indicate?

64. What do the lengths of the arrows in Figure 3 indicate?

65. If you were to draw one arrow to represent the combination of the two arrows in Figure 3, in what direction would it point?

66. According to Figure 3, how could the combination of arrows A and B be determined?

67. Assuming arrow A has a value of 70 and arrow B has a value of 50 in Figure 3, determine the effect on the dot between them. Be sure to supply the correct units.

Figure 4

68. According to Figure 4, are all of the skydivers accelerating at the same rate? Explain your answer.

69. What will cause the skydivers in Figure 4 to stop accelerating?

70. Explain the effect that open parachutes have on the velocity of the skydivers in Figure 4.

71. What is the relationship between the air resistance on the skydivers in Figure 4 and the effect of an open parachute?

CRITICAL THINKING AND APPLICATION

Discuss each of the following in a brief paragraph.

72. Explain the significance of this message radioed by the Apollo crew to mission control as the astronauts traveled toward the moon: "We would like to thank the person who made this trip possible . . . Sir Isaac Newton!"

73. Describe where you would land if you jumped straight up in the air while standing in the aisle of a moving airplane. Explain your answer in terms of one of Newton's laws of motion.

74. Explain what happens to you when a car in which you are a passenger stops quickly.

75. Use the relationship stated in Newton's second law of motion to explain why a large car gets less mileage than a small car from the same quantity of gas when both cars have the same acceleration.

76. Describe the relationships that exists between the items in the following pairs: force and mass; force and acceleration; mass and acceleration.

77. Explain how Newton's first law of motion can be considered a special case of his second law.

78. An airplane drops a flare directly over you. Does the flare hit you? Explain your answer.

79. A block of wood rests on a wooden ramp. When wheels are attached to the block of wood, it slides down the ramp. In terms of forces, friction, and motion, explain why this happens.

80. Explain why you can feel the effect of gravity between you and the Earth, but not between you and your pencil.

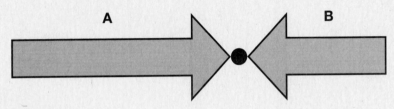

Figure 3

Figure 4

Test Bank Answer Key

1. d	15. c	29. d
2. c	16. b	30. c
3. a	17. b	31. T
4. b	18. a	32. F
5. c	19. d	33. F
6. a	20. c	34. T
7. b	21. d	35. F
8. c	22. c	36. T
9. d	23. b	37. T
10. a	24. a	38. F
11. c	25. d	39. F
12. c	26. d	40. T
13. d	27. b	
14 d	28. b	

41. force
42. 9.8 m/sec/sec
43. fluid
44. sliding
45. fluid
46. balanced
47. unbalanced
48. Isaac Newton
59. friction
50. friction
51. inertia
52. unbalanced
53. newton
54. mass
55. pairs
56. weight
57. inertia
58. gravity
59. Force
60. increases
61. Two unequal forces acting simultaneously on one mass positioned between the forces.
62. The forces are not balanced. One arrow is longer than the other.
63. The directions of the forces.
64. The strength or sizes of the forces.
65. The arrow head would point to the right.
66. Arrow B must be subtracted from Arrow A.
67. The mass will move to the right as a result of 20 N of Force A acting on it.
68. Yes. They are accelerating at a rate of 9.8 m/sec/sec, which is the acceleration due to the force of gravity between their masses and the Earth.
69. The air resistance on their masses becomes equal to the force of gravity, so the forces are then balanced.
70. The falling velocity becomes slower.
71. An open parachute provides greater air resistance; the greater the air resistance, the slower the fall (inverse relationship).

72. Answers will vary but should include Newton's three laws of motion which describe: combined forces governing zero velocity, constant velocity, acceleration, and both balanced and unbalanced forces.

73. According to Newton's first law of motion, you would land in the same spot from which you jumped, since your forward velocity is the same as that of the airplane. Your forward velocity has not been changed by any unbalanced force.

74. Your inertia keeps you moving forward, according to Newton's first law of motion. If you are wearing a seat belt, the belt pulls you in the opposite direction, serving as an unbalanced force opposing your forward motion.

75. Newton's second law of motion states that force equals mass times acceleration. More gas is needed to provide the force to accelerate a larger mass at the same acceleration as a smaller mass.

76. Force equals mass times acceleration. Force is directly proportional to both mass and acceleration. Mass is inversely proportional to acceleration.

77. Newton's second law of motion states that acceleration is produced by an unbalanced force. This implies no change in motion if forces are balanced. Newton's first law of motion refers to rest and constant velocity. Both laws are references to zero unbalanced forces: that is, to balanced forces only.

78. No. The inertia of the flare will carry it forward as it drops so that it will land in front of you.

79. Without wheels, the block of wood experiences enough sliding friction to keep it in place. That is, the frictional force between the surface of the ramp and the wood just balances the pull of gravity on the block of wood. When wheels are attached to the wood, the sliding friction changes to rolling friction, which exerts less force. Now the pull of gravity is greater than the force of friction. As a result, the block of wood rolls down the ramp.

80. The force of gravity depends upon the mass of the two objects and the distance between them. The huge mass of the Earth exhibits a strong gravitational force, while the mass of the pencil exerts such a weak gravitational force that it cannot be felt.

Contents

CHAPTER 3

Chapter Test

CHAPTER 3 ■ Forces in Fluids

MULTIPLE CHOICE

Write the letter of the correct answer on the line at the left.

_____ 1. To find pressure, you must know
   a. weight and volume.
   b. force and area.
   c. mass and area.
   d. force and mass.

_____ 2. One reason air pressure increases at lower altitudes is because
   a. there are fewer air particles in a given area.
   b. there are more air particles in a given area.
   c. the air particles have more mass.
   d. the air particles have less mass.

_____ 3. Fluids are
   a. liquids, gases, and solids.
   b. either liquids or gases.
   c. liquids.
   d. either solids or gases.

_____ 4. The brake system on a car is an example of a(an)
   a. hydraulic device.   c. lever.
   b. simple machine.   d. inclined plane.

_____ 5. What is the pressure if a force of 200 N is applied over an area of 50 cm²?
   a. 4 N/cm²   c. 10,000 N/cm²
   b. 0.24 N/cm²   d. 150 N/cm²

_____ 6. When the area over which pressure is applied is increased,
   a. the pressure decreases.
   b. the force on that area increases.
   c. the pressure increases.
   d. the pressure first increases and then decreases.

_____ 7. The buoyant force exerted by a fluid can be
   a. greater than the weight of the object.
   b. less than the weight of the object.
   c. the same as the weight of the object.
   d. all of the above

_____ 8. The pressure in a moving stream of fluid
   a. is greater than the pressure in the surrounding fluid.
   b. is less than the pressure in the surrounding fluid.
   c. depends on the nature of the fluid.
   d. depends on the volume of the fluid.

9. An airplane wing is designed to make the air move
  a. at the same speed over the top as under the bottom.
  b. slower over the top than under the bottom.
  c. faster over the top than under the bottom.
  d. slower over the top as well as under the bottom.

_____ 10. An object floats because it displaces a weight of fluid
  a. equal to or greater than its own weight.
  b. equal to its volume.
  c. less than its own weight.
  d. with a density greater than 1 g/cm³.

COMPLETION

Complete each statement on the line at the left.

_____ 1. Pressure is force divided by _____.

_____ 2. According to _____ principle, the buoyant force on an object is equal to the weight of the fluid displaced by that object.

_____ 3. Due to the force of _____, the pressure of a fluid increases as depth increases.

_____ 4. _____ is the mass of a substance divided by its volume.

_____ 5. A device called a(an) _____ is a simple tube or hose that operates by creating a difference in pressure.

TRUE OR FALSE

Determine whether each statement is true or false. If it is true, write T. If it is false, change the underlined word or words to make the statement true.

_____ _____ 1. The pressure in a moving stream of fluid is <u>more</u> than the pressure in the surrounding fluid.

_____ _____ 2. <u>Fluids</u> exert pressure in all directions.

_____ _____ 3. When the air moving over the top of an airplane wing is going faster than the air moving under the bottom of the wing, the airplane will go <u>down</u>.

_____ _____ 4. The density of water is <u>1 g/cm³</u>.

_____ _____ 5. Atmospheric pressure is measured with a device called a <u>thermometer</u>.

Name _____ Class _____ Date _____

Substance	Density (g/cm³)
Water	1.0
Wood	0.8
Steel	7.8
Mercury	13.5

1. What will happen when steel is placed in water? _____

2. What will happen when wood is placed in water? _____

3. What will happen when steel is placed in mercury? _____

4. What will happen when wood is placed in mercury? _____

5. What will happen when mercury is placed in water? _____

6. If all four substances are put in one container, how will they be arranged from top to

   bottom? _____

ESSAY

Write a brief paragraph discussing each of the following statements.

1. Explain why an object seems to lose weight when it is immersed in water.

   _____

   _____

   _____

   _____

   _____

   _____

2. Using Bernoulli's principle, explain how an airplane is able to lift up into the air.

_____

_____

_____

_____

_____

_____

3. Explain how a steel ship is able to float even though steel is more dense than water.

_____

_____

_____

_____

_____

_____

4. Explain how a hydraulic device works.

_____

_____

_____

_____

_____

_____

5. Using what you know about pressure, explain why a performer can lie on a bed of nails without getting injured.

_____

_____

_____

_____

_____

_____

Answer Key

MULTIPLE CHOICE

1. b **2.** b **3.** b **4.** a **5.** a **6.** b **7.** d **8.** b **9.** c **10.** a

COMPLETION

1. area **2.** Archimedes' **3.** gravity **4.** Density **5.** siphon

TRUE OR FALSE

1. F, less **2.** T **3.** F, up **4.** T **5.** F, barometer

USING SCIENCE SKILLS

1. It will sink. **2.** It will float. **3.** It will float. **4.** It will float. **5.** It will sink. **6.** wood, water, steel, mercury

ESSAY

1. This is caused by buoyancy, the upward force fluids exert on objects. If an object displaces the same amount of water as the weight of the object, it will float. Even though an object sinks, it displaces some water. The resulting buoyant force opposes gravity, thereby making the object seem to lose weight. **2.** As an airplane flies, air strikes the front of the wing and separates. Air traveling over the top has farther to go than air traveling under the bottom, so it must go faster to travel the same distance. The air moving faster over the top creates less pressure than the air moving under the bottom. The airplane lifts up because the pressure pushing up is greater than the pressure pushing down. **3.** A steel ship is not solid; it contains a large volume of air. The density of the steel plus the air is less than the density of water. **4.** In a hydraulic device, there are two cylinders or pistons. One piston has a large surface area. Since force equals pressure times area, the piston with the larger surface area has more force. The larger the difference between the surface areas of the two pistons, the greater is the force in the larger piston. **5.** Pressure is defined as force per unit area. The pressure exerted by an object will decrease as the force decreases or as the area over which it acts increases. When a person lies on a bed of nails, the weight of the person is distributed over a large area of nails, so no one nail is acted upon by a large force. As a result, the person will not be harmed. In contrast, if a person steps on a nail, the force applied to that one nail is great and a serious puncture wound may result.

Test Bank Test

CHAPTER 3 ■ Forces in Fluids

MULTIPLE CHOICE

Write the letter of the answer that best completes each statement.

_____ 1. Pressure is force
   a. divided by mass.   c. times mass.
   b. divided by area.   d. times area.

_____ 2. Pressure is measured in which of the following units?
   a. N/cm^2 c. N
   b. N/cm^3 d. cm^2/N

_____ 3. At high altitudes, there are
   a. more particles of air.
   b. fewer particles of air.
   c. the same number of air particles as at lower altitudes.
   d. fewer particles of air and increased air pressure.

_____ 4. Fluid pressure increases as
   a. altitude increases.   c. depth increases.
   b. altitude and depth increase. d. depth decreases.

_____ 5. The direction of fluid pressure is
   a. upward.   c. toward the sides.
   b. downward.   d. in all directions.

_____ 6. The direction of a buoyant force on an object placed in a fluid is
   a. unrelated to other forces on that object.
   b. opposite to the gravitational force on that object.
   c. in the same direction as the gravitational force on that object.
   d. in the same direction as the weight of the object.

_____ 7. Archimedes' principle applies to
   a. submerged objects only.   c. floating objects only.
   b. liquids and gases.   d. liquids only.

_____ 8. According to Archimedes' principle, the buoyant force on an object is
   a. always greater than the weight of a submerged object.
   b. greater than the weight of the displaced fluid.
   c. equal to the weight of the displaced fluid.
   d. less than the weight of the displaced fluid.

_____ 9. An object will float in a fluid if the density of the fluid is
   a. greater than the density of the object.
   b. less than the density of the object.
   c. equal to or less than the density of the object.
   d. unrelated to either the mass or the volume of the object.

_____ 10. The density of water is
   a. 1.0 g.
   b. 1.0 cm³.
   c. 1.0 g/cm³.
   d. 1.0 cm³/g.

_____ 11. When a submarine sinks,
   a. its weight is greater than the weight of the displaced water.
   b. its weight is less than the weight of the displaced water.
   c. its weight is equal to the weight of the displaced water.
   d. its weight is less than the buoyant force.

_____ 12. Although the density of steel is 7.8 g/cm³ and the density of water is 1 g/cm³, steel cruise ships float because
   a. most of the ship is steel, but part is water.
   b. the total density of the steel, air, and load is less than the density of water.
   c. the total density of the steel, air, and load is greater than the density of water.
   d. the total density of air and load is equal to the density of steel.

_____ 13. In order to float in air, balloons are filled with
   a. carbon dioxide because carbon dioxide is less dense than air.
   b. equal parts of helium and carbon dioxide.
   c. helium because helium is less dense than air.
   d. neither helium nor carbon dioxide.

_____ 14. If 51 g of a substance takes up 75 cm³ of space, the density of the substance is
   a. 1.47 g/cm³.
   b. 0.68 g/cm³.
   c. 1.47 cm³/g.
   d. 0.68 cm³/g.

_____ 15. The principle applied to the design of an airplane wing was developed by
   a. Archimedes.
   b. Bernoulli.
   c. Newton.
   d. Boyle.

_____ 16. The faster a fluid moves, the
   a. less pressure it exerts.
   b. more pressure it exerts.
   c. less is its density.
   d. greater is its density.

_____ 17. Because the density of salt water is greater than that of fresh water, a ship will
   a. float higher in salt water than in fresh water.
   b. float higher in fresh water than in salt water.
   c. be submerged more rapidly in salt water than in an equal amount of fresh water.
   d. require more salt water than fresh water to equal its weight.

_____ 18. Comparing the densities of hot and cold air, hot air
   a. is equal in density to cold air.
   b. is more dense than cold air.
   c. is less dense than cold air.
   d. has particles closer together.

_____ 19. An example of a hydraulic system is
   a. a person floating in a salty body of water.
   b. a hot air balloon.
   c. a ball bearing.
   d. the lift on a barber's chair.

_____ **20.** Buoyancy is
   a. the tendency of objects to sink in fluids.
   b. the force of a fluid that pushes an object up.
   c. a force in the same direction as gravity.
   d. caused by the fact that objects have less mass in a fluid.

_____ **21.** An object will float in water if its density is
   a. 0.8 g/cm³.   c. 2.0 g/cm³.
   b. 1.1 g/cm³.   d. 1.5 g/cm³.

_____ **22.** What is the pressure if a force of 20 N is exerted over an area of 10 cm²?
   a. 2 N/cm²   c. 20 N/cm²
   b. 10 N/cm²   d. 200 N/cm²

_____ **23.** What is the force exerted on a surface measuring 1000 cm² if the pressure is
   2 N/cm²?
   a. 500 N   c. 2000 N
   b. 500 cm   d. 2000 cm

_____ **24.** Which of the following would cause an increase in pressure?
   a. increasing the area without changing force
   b. decreasing the area without changing force
   c. decreasing the force without changing area
   d. decreasing both force and area by the same amount

_____ **25.** Hydraulic devices apply a small force over a small area to
   a. ensure that the pressure is equal in all directions.
   b. produce a large force over a large area.
   c. increase pressure.
   d. produce a large force over a small area.

_____ **26.** The pressure exerted by a fluid is due to the motion of its particles and the
   a. downward pull of gravity on them.
   b. volume of the substance.
   c. color of the substance.
   d. friction of the substance.

_____ **27.** An airplane wing is designed to make the air move
   a. faster over the top than under the bottom.
   b. slower over the top than under the bottom.
   c. the same speed over the top as under the bottom.
   d. slower both over the top and under the bottom.

_____ **28.** A submarine submerges by
   a. taking in more water.
   b. decreasing its speed.
   c. decreasing its density.
   d. decreasing its mass.

_____ **29.** Fluids will move
   a. from areas of higher pressure to areas of lower pressure.
   b. from areas of lower pressure to areas of higher pressure.
   c. both of these
   d. neither of these

_____ **30.** Density equals
   a. volume divided by mass. c. mass divided by volume.
   b. mass times volume. d. volume minus mass.

TRUE OR FALSE

Determine whether each statement is true or false.

_____ **31.** The upward buoyant force of a fluid opposes the downward force of gravity on an object.

_____ **32.** Fluids exert pressure because their particles have weight, although they are motionless.

_____ **33.** Submarines could be crushed due to the increase in fluid pressure at certain ocean depths.

_____ **34.** The buoyant force on an object is equal to the weight of the fluid displaced by the object.

_____ **35.** Buoyancy determines whether an object sinks or floats in fluids.

_____ **36.** A hydraulic lift transmits fluid pressure in different amounts in different directions.

_____ **37.** The total area of both pistons in a hydraulic lift is the same.

_____ **38.** The particles in fluids are tightly packed together.

_____ **39.** As depth in a fluid increases, the pressure it exerts decreases.

_____ **40.** The relationship between buoyancy and the weight of a displaced fluid is called Archimedes' principle.

COMPLETION

Fill in the word or number that best completes each statement.

_____ **41.** A fluid exerts a force called _____ on the walls of its container.

_____ **42.** Bernoulli's principle states that the pressure in a moving stream of fluid is _____ than the pressure in the surrounding fluid.

_____ **43.** As altitude increases, air pressure _____.

_____ **44.** The upward force of a fluid pushing on objects is called _____.

_____ **45.** Water that has been moved aside by an object immersed in it has been _____.

_____ **46.** If the buoyant force of a liquid is greater than the weight of an immersed object, that object will _____.

_____ **47.** Because the surface area of the one piston of a hydraulic lift is larger than the other piston, the larger piston produces a larger _____.

_____ **48.** Force per unit area defines _____.

_____ **49.** The pressure exerted by fluids in motion is described in the principle developed by _____.

_____ **50.** The air passing below an airplane wing travels _____ than air above it.

_____ **51.** _____ pressure is exerted equally in all directions.

_____ **52.** The _____ is a muscle in the chest cavity that tightens and relaxes to allow you to breathe.

_____ **53.** The brakes on a car are an example of a(an) _____ device.

_____ **54.** The density of water is _____.

_____ **55.** An object with a density of 2.7 g/cm³ will _____ in water.

_____ **56.** Suction is due to _____ air pressure in two different locations.

_____ **57.** One reason air pressure decreases with increased altitudes is because the number of fluid particles in a given area _____.

_____ **58.** The buoyant force on an object immersed in a fluid is equal to or greater than that object's _____ if the object floats.

_____ **59.** Hydraulic devices use the principle that the addition of pressure to a confined fluid is transmitted in all directions _____.

_____ **60.** When you suck on a straw, the pressure inside the straw becomes _____ than standard air pressure.

Use the skills you have developed in the chapter to answer each question.

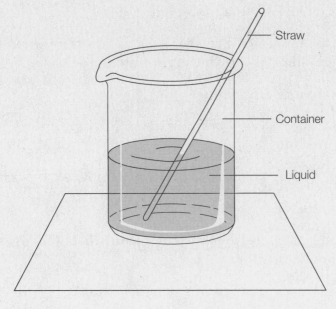

Figure 5

61. What happens to the air pressure in the straw in Figure 5 if suction is applied to the straw?

62. What condition does suction on the straw in Figure 5 create?

63. What is the effect that suction has on the liquid in the container in Figure 5?

64. If the air pressure inside the container in Figure 5 were greater than the air pressure outside the container, what would happen?

65. Does the liquid in the container in Figure 5 exert any pressure? If so, on what?

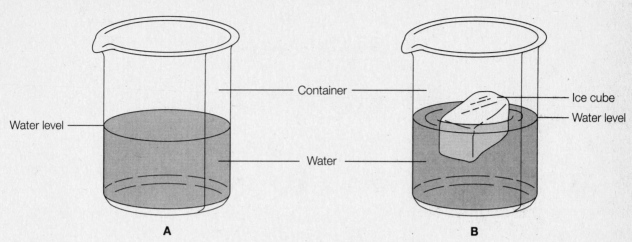

Figure 6

66. Why is there a difference in the water levels in containers A and B in Figure 6?

67. What is the force that causes the ice cube in container B in Figure 6 to float?

68. Referring to Figure 6, how does the force that causes the ice cube to float relate to the amount of change in the water level?

69. Who explained how the buoyant force is related to the displaced fluid illustrated in Figure 6?

70. Is the result in container B in Figure 6 affected by the container? Explain your answer.

71. Does the ice cube in container B in Figure 6 exert a force on the water? If so, identify it.

72. Describe the kinds of pressure that exist in container B in Figure 6 and the effect of these pressures.

CRITICAL THINKING AND APPLICATION

Discuss each of the following in a brief paragraph.

73. In terms of the liquid displaced, explain why a solid mass may sink in a liquid. Why a solid mass may float in liquid?

74. Explain why hot air balloons rise and fall in a single substance such as air.

75. Explain why a light push applied to the brake pedal of a car that weighs 10,000 N can stop the car.

76. Explain the relationship between pressure, force, and area.

77. Why must the inside of a submarine be pressurized?

78. Explain why an airplane gains additional lift when the flaps at the rear of the wings are in their downward position.

79. Using the principle of fluid pressure, explain how a vacuum cleaner works.

80. Why does air enter your lungs when you inhale? Why does air leave your lungs when you exhale?

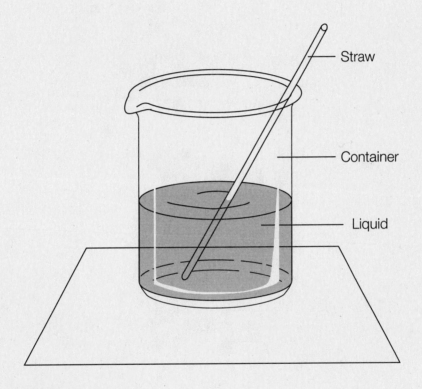

Straw

Container

Liquid

Figure 5

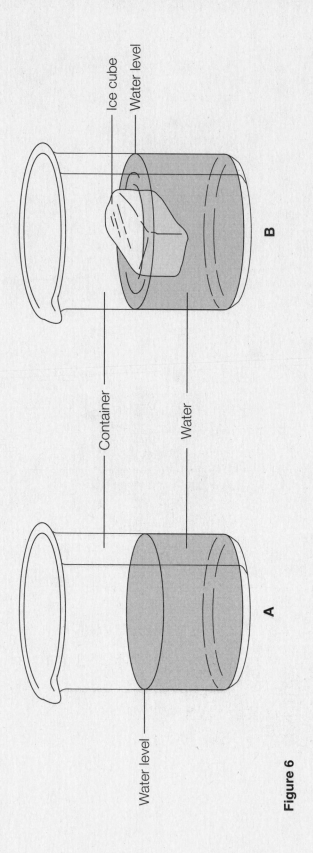

Figure 6

Test Bank Answer Key

1. b
2. a
3. b
4. c
5. d
6. b
7. b
8. c
9. a
10. c
11. a
12. b
13. c
14. b

15. b
16. a
17. a
18. c
19. d
20. b
21. a
22. a
23. c
24. b
25. b
26. a
27. a
28. a

29. a
30. c
31. T
32. F
33. T
34. T
35. T
36. F
37. F
38. F
39. F
40. T

41. pressure
42. less
43. decreases
44. buoyancy
45. displaced
46. float
47. force
48. pressure
49. Bernoulli
50. slower
51. Fluid
52. diaphragm
53. hydraulic
54. 1 g/cm3
55. sink
56. unequal
57. decreases
58. weight
59. equally
60. less
61. Air pressure is reduced.
62. unequal air pressure
63. Because of suction, the air pressure on the liquid in the container is greater than that in the straw, causing the liquid in the container to rise in the straw.
64. The container would break.
65. Yes. On the straw, the container, and the air
66. The ice cube in container B has displaced some of the water, causing the water level to rise.
67. buoyancy
68. The amount of change in the water level is the volume of displaced water. The weight of the displaced water is equal to the buoyant force of the liquid on the ice cube.
69. Archimedes
70. No. Ice is less dense than water and will always float in a characteristic way in a liquid of greater density like water.
71. Yes. Gravitational force (weight)

72. The downward pressure of air on the water and the ice cube is balanced by upward pressure of the water and the ice cube. Pressure is directly proportional to force. The weight force of the water displaced by the ice cube is related to the buoyant force of the water.

73. A mass will sink in a liquid if the weight of the displaced liquid is less than the weight of the mass. A mass will float if the weight of the displaced liquid is equal to or greater than the weight of the mass.

74. Air inside the balloon is heated, giving that air a density that is less than that of the air outside. The balloon will rise. When the air inside the balloon is cooled, its density increases. When the density of air inside the balloon is greater than the density of the air outside the balloon, the balloon will fall.

75. According to the principle of hydraulics, pressure is transmitted equally in all directions throughout a liquid. The retarding force of the brake pedal is distributed equally into brake fluid. A large piston serves to multiply the brake force into a much larger force—one great enough to stop the car.

76. Pressure is equal to force divided by area. Pressure and force are directly proportional to each other. Pressure and area are inversely proportional to each other.

77. The inside of a submarine must be pressurized in order to oppose the tremendous outside pressure applied to the submarine by deep ocean waters. However, pressurized submarines are still limited to certain depths of water.

78. When the flaps are in the downward position, the air passing under the wing encounters increased resistance and moves slower. The air passing over the wing moves faster than the air below the wing and lift increases.

79. A fan inside the vacuum cleaner reduces the air pressure inside the cleaner. The greater outside air pressure will then push the air and surrounding dirt into the vacuum cleaner.

80. As you inhale, the diaphragm moves downward, increasing the size of the chest cavity and lungs and decreasing the air pressure within them. Air from the outside will then rush into the lungs. As you exhale, the diaphragm moves upward, decreasing the size of the chest cavity and the lungs and increasing the air pressure within them. The air will now move out of the lungs.

Contents

Chapter Test

CHAPTER 4 ■ Work, Power, and Simple Machines

MULTIPLE CHOICE

Write the letter of the correct answer on the line at the left.

_____ 1. A force exerted over a distance to move an object is
a. measured in newtons. c. velocity.
b. momentum. d. work.

_____ 2. The amount of work done by two boys who apply 200 N of force in an unsuccessful attempt to move a stalled car is
a. 400 N-m. c. 400 N.
b. 0. d. 200 N-m.

_____ 3. A unit used to measure force is a
a. newton. c. joule.
b. newton-meter. d. watt.

_____ 4. The mechanical advantage of a machine is the number of time it
a. multiplies the resistance force.
b. multiples the effort force.
c. changes the direction of the effort force.
d. changes the direction of the resistance force.

_____ 5. A fulcrum is
a. a support for an inclined plane.
b. the place where a lever is supported.
c. measured in newton-meters.
d. measured in joules.

_____ 6. Which of the following is *not* a third-class lever?
a. scissors c. baseball bat
b. broom d. shovel

_____ 7. The advantage of using a third-class lever is that it
a. multiplies effort force.
b. makes the resistance force smaller.
c. multiplies distance.
d. decreases distance.

_____ 8. Power equals work
a. divided by time.
b. divided by weight.
c. divided by distance.
d. times distance.

_____ **9.** A movable pulley can
   a. change the direction of the force.
   b. multiply force.
   c. multiply distance.
   d. have a mechanical advantage of less than one.

_____ **10.** An example of a compound machine is a
   a. pair of scissors.
   b. pair of pliers.
   c. hammer.
   d. typewriter.

COMPLETION

Complete each statement on the line at the left.

_____ **1.** A newton-meter is a measure of work also known as the _____.

_____ **2.** The unit of power is the _____.

_____ **3.** A simple machine that is a straight slanted surface is a(an) _____.

_____ **4.** Any device that makes work easier is called a(an) _____.

_____ **5.** A(An) _____ is an inclined plane that moves.

TRUE OR FALSE

Determine whether each statement is true or false. If it is true, write T. If it is false, change the underlined word or words to make the statement true.

_____ _____ **1.** The comparison of work output to work input is called the mechanical advantage.

_____ _____ **2.** The work done by a machine is called the work output.

_____ _____ **3.** A second-class lever will always multiply distance.

_____ _____ **4.** A screw is an inclined plane wrapped around a cylinder.

_____ _____ **5.** A wheel and axle is a chain, belt, or rope wrapped around a wheel.

USING SCIENCE SKILLS: Interpreting a Graph

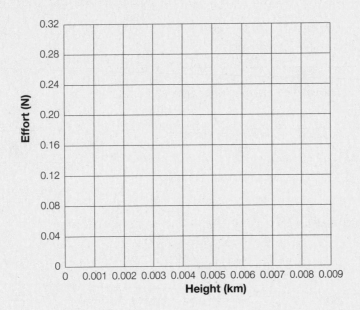

The following data were collected when a resistance weighing 0.30 N was moved up an inclined plane measuring 0.0075 km in length. Plot the data on the graph. Draw a straight line connecting the dots you have plotted.

Height of inclined plane (km)	Amount of effort needed to move the resistance (N)
.001	.04
.002	.08
.003	.12
.004	.16
.005	.20

1. According to the graph, how much effort would be required to lift the resistance when

   the height of the incline was 0.0025 km? _____

   How much effort would be needed at 0.0055km? _____

2. What happens to the amount of effort needed to lift the resistance as the height of the

   inclined plane is increased? _____

Extend the line on the graph all the way to the top of the graph. This is called extrapolation. Extrapolation will enable you to predict values that have not actually been measured, based on the information that has already been collected.

3. Using this extended line, predict how much effort would be needed to lift the resistance if the height of the inclined plane was raised to 0.0075 km. _____

_____

4. What would the mechanical advantage of the inclined plane be at this point? _____

_____

5. An inclined plane will always multiply your force. Explain this.

_____

_____

ESSAY

Write a brief paragraph discussing each of the following statements.

1. A porter carries a 25 kg suitcase a distance of 1 km. Explain why he does no work.

_____

_____

_____

_____

_____

_____

_____

2. Explain how a first-class lever can sometimes be used to multiply force and sometimes be used to multiply distance.

_____

_____

_____

_____

_____

_____

_____

3. Explain why a second-class lever will always multiply force and a third-class lever will always multiply distance.

_____

_____

_____

_____

_____

_____

4. Explain why wedges and screws are special types of inclined planes.

_____

_____

_____

_____

_____

_____

_____

5. Compare simple machines to compound machines.

_____

_____

_____

_____

_____

_____

_____

Answer Key

MULTIPLE CHOICE

1. d 2. b 3. a 4. b 5. b 6. a 7. c 8. a 9. b 10. d

COMPLETION

1. joule 2. watt 3. inclined plane 4. machine 5. wedge

TRUE OR FALSE

1. F, efficiency 2. T 3. F, effort force 4. T 5. F, pulley

USING SCIENCE SKILLS

1. 0.10 N; 0.22 N 2. It increases. 3. 0.30 N 4. one 5. The length of an inclined plane will always be greater than the height. Since the effort force is being moved a greater distance, the effort force will be multiplied.

ESSAY

1. To do work, an effort force must be applied through a distance. The distance must be in the same direction as the force. The porter applied a force to pick up the suitcase. At this time he does work. However, when he starts moving forward, the force and distance are no longer in the same direction so he does no work. 2. If the fulcrum of a first-class lever is placed close to the resistance force, the distance over which the effort force is exerted is greater, therefore the lever will multiply the force. If the fulcrum is placed close to the effort force, the distance over which the effort force is exerted is smaller, therefore the lever will multiply distance. 3. A second-class lever has the resistance force between the fulcrum and the effort force. Since the effort force is moved over a larger distance, a second-class lever will always multiply the force. A third-class lever has the effort force between the fulcrum and the resistance force. Since the effort force is moved over a smaller distance, a third-class lever will always multiply the distance. 4. A wedge is shaped like a double inclined plane. Knife edges and other sharpened edges are sloped like an inclined plane. Like an inclined plane, the longer and thinner the wedge is, the less effort is needed to overcome the resistance. A screw is an inclined plane wrapped around a cylinder to form a spiral. 5. There are six simple machines: the lever, the inclined plane, the wheel and axle, the pulley, the screw, and the wedge. A compound machine is a combination of two or more simple machines. Compound machines, like simple machines, cannot put out more work than is put into them.

Test Bank Test

CHAPTER 4 ■ Work, Power, and Simple Machines

MULTIPLE CHOICE

Write the letter of the answer that best completes each statement.

_____ **1.** An example of work being done is
　　a. a box being carried a distance.
　　b. a person pushing against a closed door that remains closed.
　　c. a person pushing a lawn mower and cutting the grass.
　　d. all of the above

_____ **2.** Work divided by time equals
　　a. force.　　　　　　　c. power.
　　b. distance.　　　　　 d. mass.

_____ **3.** The work input of a crowbar is equal to the
　　a. force applied to the handle.
　　b. distance the handle moves.
　　c. force applied to the handle times the distance the handle moves.
　　d. force applied by the resistance times the distance through which this force is applied.

_____ **4.** Machines
　　a. multiply work.
　　b. multiply force or distance.
　　c. apply an effort force.
　　d. make work output greater than work input.

_____ **5.** Without friction there would be
　　a. less machine efficiency.
　　b. greater work output than work input.
　　c. greater work input than work output.
　　d. equal work input and output.

_____ **6.** A ramp is a simple machine called the
　　a. wedge.　　　　　　 c. pulley.
　　b. inclined plane.　　　d. lever.

_____ **7.** Sharpening a wedge
　　a. decreases the mechanical advantage.
　　b. increases the effort force.
　　c. decreases the mechanical advantage and increases the effort force.
　　d. increases the mechanical advantage and decreases the effort force.

_____ **8.** For work to be done, the direction of
　　a. motion must be perpendicular to the direction of the applied force.
　　b. the applied force must be opposite to the direction of motion.
　　c. the applied force must be perpendicular to the direction of motion.
　　d. the applied force must be the same as the direction of motion.

　　　　　　　　　　　　　　　 Motion, Forces, and Energy　**S** ■ **81**

_____ **9.** Work is force times
  a. area.   c. weight.
  b. distance.   d. mass.

_____ **10.** The amount of work done when a force of 300 N moves an object a distance of 2 m is
  a. 600 N.   c. 150 N.
  b. 600 N-m.   d. 150 N-m.

_____ **11.** A unit of power is a
  a. newton.   c. meter.
  b. newton-meter.   d. watt.

_____ **12.** Work output equals the resistance force
  a. times the distance through which the output force is applied.
  b. divided by the distance through which the force is applied.
  c. divided by the effort force.
  d. times the effort force.

_____ **13.** The number of times a machine multiplies effort force is
  a. momentum of the machine.   c. power of the machine.
  b. mechanical advantage.   d. resistance of the machine.

_____ **14.** An inclined plane that moves is called a
  a. lever.   c. wedge.
  b. pulley.   d. wheel.

_____ **15.** The work done by a person lifting a 100-N suitcase a distance of 2 m is
  a. 200 N-m.   c. 50 N-m.
  b. 300 J.   d. 150 N-m.

_____ **16.** The efficiency of a machine can be increased by reducing
  a. effort force.
  b. resistance force.
  c. the distance through which effort force is applied.
  d. friction.

_____ **17.** When an inclined plane is used,
  a. a greater force is exerted over a shorter distance.
  b. a smaller force is exerted over a longer distance.
  c. a mechanical advantage of less than one can result.
  d. the mechanical advantage increases as the height of the slope increases.

_____ **18.** A unit used to measure work is a
  a. newton.   c. meter.
  b. newton-meter.   d. watt.

_____ **19.** If a machine has a mechanical advantage of one, it
  a. multiplies effort.   c. multiplies resistance.
  b. reduces effort.   d. may change the direction of the force.

_____ **20.** One joule of work is the same as one
  a. newton.   c. meter.
  b. newton-meter.   d. watt.

_____ **21.** A screw multiplies effort by
   a. acting through a long distance.
   b. reducing the amount of resistance force.
   c. reducing the amount of friction.
   d. adding effort force.

_____ **22.** The place at which a lever is supported is called a
   a. joule.   c. watt.
   b. newton-meter.   d. fulcrum.

_____ **23.** In a second-class lever, the
   a. fulcrum is between the effort force and resistance force.
   b. effort force is between the resistance force and fulcrum.
   c. resistance force is between the effort force and fulcrum.
   d. none of these

_____ **24.** A wedge is a moving
   a. wheel and axle.   c. pulley.
   b. lever.   d. inclined plane.

_____ **25.** A chain, belt, or rope wrapped around a wheel is called a(an)
   a. wheel and axle.   c. inclined plane.
   b. pulley.   d. lever.

_____ **26.** A simple machine made up of two circular objects of different sizes is called a(an)
   a. wheel and axle.   c. inclined plane.
   b. pulley.   d. lever.

_____ **27.** Which of the following is *not* a first-class lever?
   a. scissors   c. crowbar
   b. wheelbarrow   d. pliers

_____ **28.** In a third-class lever, the
   a. fulcrum is between the effort force and the resistance force.
   b. effort force is between the resistance force and the fulcrum.
   c. resistance force is between the effort force and the fulcrum.
   d. none of these

_____ **29.** No machine has 100 percent efficiency due to
   a. resistance forces.
   b. an increase in distance.
   c. friction.
   d. none of these

_____ **30.** The comparison of work input to work output is called
   a. resistance force.
   b. efficiency.
   c. effort force.
   d. mechanical advantage.

TRUE OR FALSE

Determine whether each statement is true or false.

_____ **31.** You do work on an object if you hold it for a period of time.

_____ **32.** Work is the product of force times distance.

_____ **33.** All machines make work easier by changing the direction of the applied force.

_____ **34.** The efficiency of a machine is never 100 percent.

_____ **35.** The length of an inclined plane is never shorter than its height.

_____ **36.** The fixed point about which a lever is free to pivot is called the fulcrum.

_____ **37.** More work output than work input is the result of using a compound machine.

_____ **38.** When a lever is used to pry up a rock, the rock's weight represents the effort force.

_____ **39.** A machine is any device which makes work easier.

_____ **40.** A wheel and axle is an example of a compound machine.

COMPLETION

Fill in the word or number that best completes each statement.

_____ **41.** Work is defined as a force acting through a(an) _____.

_____ **42.** One joule is equal to one _____.

_____ **43.** The rate at which work is done is called _____.

_____ **44.** Power is measured in _____.

_____ **45.** The minimum number of different forces involved in the use of machines is _____.

_____ **46.** The force applied by the machine is called the _____ force.

_____ **47.** The force applied to the machine is called the _____ force.

_____ **48.** The ratio of the work output of a machine to the work input is called the _____ of the machine.

_____ **49.** A jar lid is an example of a simple machine called a _____.

_____ **50.** The six simple machines are the screw, the pulley, the lever, the wedge, the wheel and axle, and the _____.

_____ **51.** A(An) _____ pulley multiplies effort force.

_____ **52.** A bicycle is an example of a combination of simple machines called a(an) _____ machine.

_____ **53.** A seesaw is an example of a _____ lever.

_____ **54.** The efficiency of a machine is reduced by the force called _____.

_____ **55.** The fulcrum is between the effort force and the resistance force on a _____ lever.

_____ **56.** A wheelbarrow is an example of a _____ lever.

_____ **57.** A pulley that is attached to a structure is called a(an) _____ pulley.

_____ **58.** A moving inclined plane is called a(an) _____.

_____ **59.** A doorknob is an example of a simple machine called a(an) _____.

_____ **60.** A(An) _____ pulley only changes the direction of the effort force.

USING SCIENCE SKILLS

Use the skills you have developed in the chapter to answer each question.

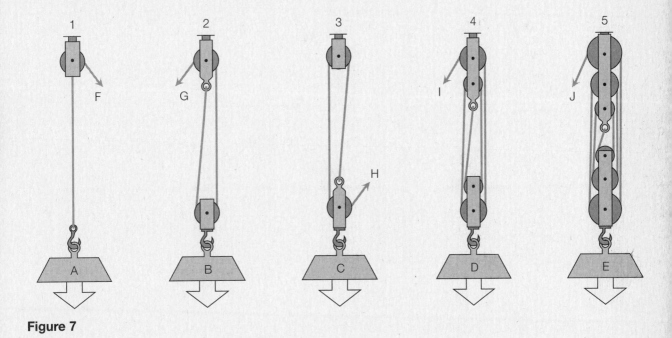

Figure 7

61. Is machine 1 in Figure 7 classified as a simple or compound machine?

62. What kind of machine is illustrated in Figure 7?

63. Referring to machine 2 in Figure 7, which letter represents the effort force? The resistance force?

64. Which machine in Figure 7 represents a machine that only changes the direction of the effort force?

65. Which examples in Figure 7 multiply effort force?

66. Which machine in Figure 7 has the greatest mechanical advantage?

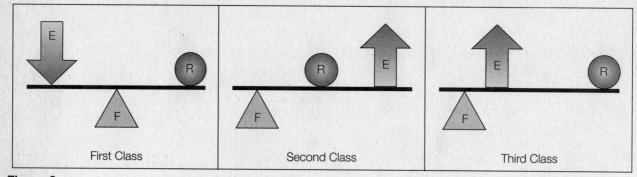

Figure 8

67. What type of simple machine is illustrated in Figure 8?

68. What do the letters E, R, and F represent in Figure 8?

69. According to Figure 8, to which class would a pair of scissors belong? Explain your answer.

70. According to Figure 8, which class does not multiply force? Why? What is its advantage as a simple machine?

71. According to Figure 8, to which class does each of the following belong: (a) fishing pole, (b) door, (c) bottle opener, (d) pliers, (e) shovel?

CRITICAL THINKING AND APPLICATION

Discuss each of the following in a brief paragraph.

72. Explain who is doing more work and why: a bricklayer carrying bricks and placing them on the wall of a building being constructed, or a project supervisor observing and recording the progress of the workers from an observation booth.

73. How much work is done in pushing an object 7 m across a floor with a force of 50 N and then pushing it back to its original position? How much power is used if this work is done in 20 sec?

74. Using a single fixed pulley, how heavy a load could you lift? Explain your answer.

75. Give an example of a machine in which friction is both an advantage and a disadvantage.

76. Is it possible to have a machine with 100 percent efficiency? Explain your answer.

77. What is effort force? Work input? Explain the relationship between effort force, effort distance, and work input.

78. For many years, people have tried to build a perpetual motion machine—a machine that could continue to run forever. No one has succeeded. Explain why.

79. You are asked to put a very heavy box onto the back of a truck. What simple machine would you use to make the task easier? Explain why you selected that machine.

80. List three ways in which a simple machine can make work easier.

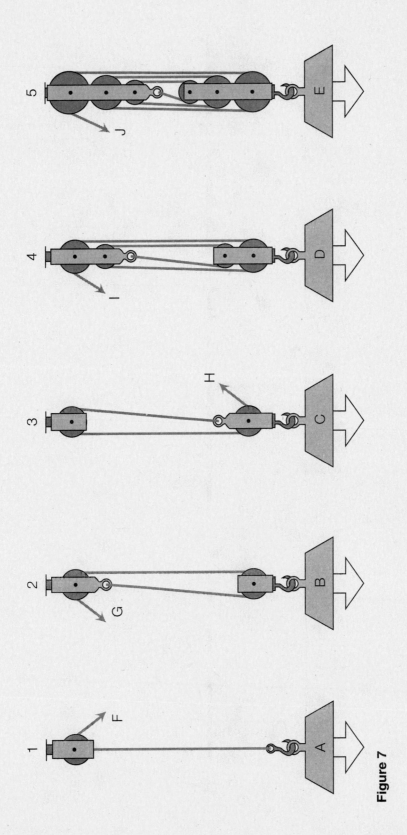

Figure 7

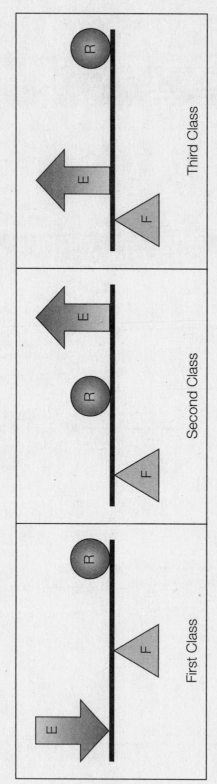

Figure 8

Test Bank Answer Key

MULTIPLE CHOICE

1. c	15. a	29. c
2. c	16. d	30. b
3. c	17. b	31. F
4. b	18. b	32. T
5. d	19. d	33. F
6. b	20. b	34. T
7. d	21. a	35. T
8. d	22. d	36. T
9. b	23. c	37. F
10. b	24. d	38. F
11. d	25. b	39. T
12. a	26. a	40. F
13. b	27. b	
14. c	28. b	

41. distance
42. newton-meter
43. power
44. watts
45. two
46. output
47. effort
48. efficiency
49. screw
50. inclined plane
51. movable
52. compound
53. first-class
54. friction
55. first-class
56. second-class
57. fixed
58. wedge
59. wheel and axle
60. fixed
61. simple machine
62. pulleys
63. The effort force is G. The resistance force is B.
64. machine 1
65. machines 2, 3, 4, and 5
66. Machine 5. As more pulleys are used, more sections of rope support the resistance force. This increases the mechanical advantage.
67. lever
68. E = effort force; R = resistance force; F = fulcrum
69. First, because the fulcrum is between the effort force and the resistance force.
70. Third. The effort force is greater than the resistance force. It multiplies the distance of the effort force.

71. (a) third (b) second (c) second (d) first (e) third
72. Work is defined as a force applied to an object, moving that object a distance in the direction of the applied force. The bricklayer is doing more work.
73. Work = 7 m × 50 N × 2 = 700 N-m or J; Power = 700 N-m/20 sec = 35 W
74. Since a fixed pulley has a mechanical advantage of one, it will only change the direction of the force applied to it. You would be able to lift a load equal to your own weight, minus the negative effects of friction.
75. Answers will vary, but one answer might be the use of a car jack. Advantage of friction: It allows a car to be raised to a desired height without slipping. Disadvantage of friction: It reduces efficiency.
76. Friction lowers the efficiency of a machine. Work output is always less than work input, so an actual machine cannot be 100 percent efficient.
77. The effort force is the force applied to a machine. Work input is the work done on a machine. The work input of a machine is equal to the effort force times the distance over which the effort force is exerted.
78. A perpetual motion machine cannot be built because the operation of any machine always involves some friction. Because the machine must expend work to overcome friction, it eventually runs down.
79. Answers will vary, but make sure the machine is an aid in lifting, such as an inclined plane or a pulley system.
80. A machine can make work easier by multiplying force, multiplying distance, or changing the direction of a force.

Contents

CHAPTER 5

Chapter Test

CHAPTER 5 ■ Energy: Forms and Changes

MULTIPLE CHOICE

Write the letter of the correct answer on the line at the left.

_____ 1. A joule is a measure of
    a. energy.   c. density.
    b. distance.   d. volume.

_____ 2. Mechanical energy is associated with
    a. chemical reactions.   c. the internal motion of particles of matter.
    b. the nuclei of atoms.   d. motion.

_____ 3. Electromagnetic energy is associated with
    a. chemical reactions.   c. the motion of electric charges.
    b. the nuclei of atoms.   d. motion.

_____ 4. Heat energy is associated with
    a. position or shape.
    b. holding together the nuclei of atoms.
    c. the internal motion of particles of matter.
    d. motion.

_____ 5. Chemical energy is
    a. energy that bonds atoms or ions together.
    b. contained in the nuclei of atoms.
    c. a result of the motion of electric charges.
    d. a result of the internal motion of particles of matter.

_____ 6. Nuclear energy is
    a. energy that bonds atoms or ions together.
    b. contained in the nuclei of atoms.
    c. a result of the motion of electric charges.
    d. a result of the internal motion of particles of matter.

_____ 7. An example of stored chemical energy is
    a. gasoline in an automobile.
    b. an electric motor.
    c. the sun's energy.
    d. light.

_____ 8. An object's kinetic energy varies with its
    a. mass and volume.
    b. mass and weight.
    c. volume and velocity.
    d. mass and velocity.

_____ **9.** Which of the following is *not* an example of an object with potential energy?
   a. car battery
   b. diver prepared to jump off a diving board
   c. wrecking ball
   d. moving baseball

_____ **10.** The factor that has the greatest effect on kinetic energy is
   a. mass.   c. velocity.
   b. weight.   d. density.

COMPLETION

Complete each statement on the line at the left.

_____ **1.** _____ is the ability to do work.

_____ **2.** The energy of position is called _____ energy.

_____ **3.** When the nucleus of an atom splits, _____ energy is released in the
                        form of heat energy and light energy.

_____ **4.** Gravitational potential energy equals weight times _____.

_____ **5.** Changes in the forms of energy are called _____.

TRUE OR FALSE

Determine whether each statement is true or false. If it is true, write T. If it is false, change
the underlined word or words to make the statement true.

_____ _____ **1.** The law of conservation of energy states that energy can be
                             neither created nor destroyed by ordinary means.

_____ _____ **2.** Energy stored in an object is called kinetic energy.

_____ _____ **3.** All forms of energy can be converted to other forms.

_____ _____ **4.** The sun's energy source is chemical energy.

_____ _____ **5.** Mechanical energy is the most concentrated form of energy.

Name _____ Class _____ Date _____

USING SCIENCE SKILLS: Interpreting a Diagram

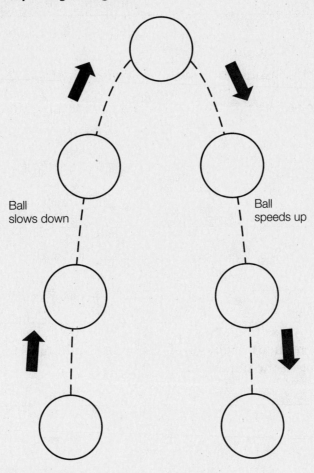

Ball
slows down

Ball
speeds up

1. Where does the ball have maximum kinetic energy?

_____

_____

2. Where does the ball have maximum potential energy?

_____

_____

3. Where does the ball have zero kinetic energy?

_____

_____

4. What happens to the potential energy of the ball as it falls?

_____

_____

5. As the ball goes up toward its maximum height, what is happening to its kinetic energy?

_____

_____

ESSAY

Write a brief paragraph discussing each of the following statements.

1. Describe the kinetic-potential conversions that occur as a pendulum swings from side to side.

_____

_____

_____

_____

_____

2. Explain why an ocean liner traveling at 100 km/hr would have more kinetic energy than a yacht traveling at the same velocity.

_____

_____

_____

_____

_____

3. Explain the relationship between mass and energy.

_____

_____

_____

_____

_____

4. Identify the five forms of energy and give an example of each.

_____

_____

_____

_____

_____

_____

5. The five forms of energy can be either kinetic or potential energy. Explain why both kinetic and potential energy are often treated as kinds of mechanical energy.

_____

_____

_____

_____

_____

_____

Answer Key

MULTIPLE CHOICE

1. a **2.** d **3.** c **4.** c **5.** a **6.** b **7.** a **8.** d **9.** d **10.** c

COMPLETION

1. Energy **2.** potential **3.** nuclear **4.** height **5.** energy conversion

TRUE OR FALSE

1. T **2.** F, potential **3.** T **4.** F, nuclear **5.** F, nuclear

USING SCIENCE SKILLS

1. at the bottom of its fall **2.** at its maximum height **3.** at the top of its path **4.** Potential energy is converted to kinetic energy. **5.** It is decreasing.

ESSAY

1. A pendulum has its greatest potential energy at the top of its arc. As it swings down, its potential energy decreases while its kinetic energy increases. The pendulum reaches its maximum kinetic energy at the bottom of its swing. As it sweeps up the opposite side, its kinetic energy decreases while its potential energy increases. **2.** Kinetic energy depends on the mass of an object and the square of its velocity. An ocean liner may travel at the same velocity as a yacht, but it has a great deal more mass. **3.** Energy is directly proportional to mass. A small amount of mass can produce a tremendous amount of energy. **4.** Mechanical energy is energy associated with motion. Water in a waterfall has mechanical energy. The internal motion of particles of matter is called heat energy. Two substances rubbing against each other produce heat energy. The energy that bonds atoms together is chemical energy. Gasoline contains chemical energy. Electromagnetic energy is produced by moving electric charges. Electric motors are driven by electromagnetic energy. Nuclear energy comes from the nuclei of atoms. The sun uses nuclear energy. **5.** All five forms of energy can have kinetic and potential energy. A flashlight battery contains chemical potential energy. Light and heat from the sun are examples of kinetic energy. However, both kinetic and potential energy most often have to do with motion, so they are often treated as kinds of mechanical energy.

Test Bank Test

CHAPTER 5 ■ Energy: Forms and Changes

MULTIPLE CHOICE

Write the letter of the answer that best completes each statement.

_____ **1.** Energy is defined as
    a. power.
    b. the ability to produce heat.
    c. a change in motion.
    d. the ability to do work or cause change.

_____ **2.** Mechanical energy is converted into heat energy when
    a. food is stored in fat cells.
    b. hands are rubbed together.
    c. charcoal is burned in a grill.
    d. lasers are used to make a colorful display.

_____ **3.** The most concentrated form of energy is
    a. nuclear.
    b. electromagnetic.
    c. chemical.
    d. heat.

_____ **4.** Potential energy is energy that is
    a. in motion.
    b. stored.
    c. not capable of doing work.
    d. not capable of causing change.

_____ **5.** Kinetic energy is energy that is
    a. in motion.
    b. stored.
    c. not capable of doing work.
    d. not capable of causing change.

_____ **6.** The kind of energy released when atoms are rearranged to form new bonds is called
    a. mechanical.
    b. electromagnetic.
    c. chemical.
    d. nuclear.

_____ **7.** The energy in the fuel of a rocket engine is
    a. kinetic energy.
    b. nuclear energy.
    c. mechanical energy.
    d. chemical potential energy.

_____ **8.** An archer's stretched bow has energy of
    a. motion.
    b. position.
    c. the kinetic type.
    d. velocity.

_____ **9.** The kinetic energy of an object increases as the object
    a. slows down.
    b. loses mass.
    c. stops moving.
    d. speeds up.

_____ **10.** An example of an object with kinetic energy is a
    a. car stopped at a red light.
    b. boulder about to fall off a cliff.
    c. skier hurtling through the air.
    d. photograph of a bicycle race.

_____ **11.** Raising or lowering a flag on a pole changes its
    a. potential energy.
    b. kinetic energy.
    c. nuclear energy.
    d. chemical energy.

_____ **12.** Kinetic energy depends upon
    a. velocity only.
    b. mass only
    c. mass and velocity.
    d. position.

_____ **13.** Gravitational potential energy depends upon
    a. height only.
    b. velocity only.
    c. mass and velocity.
    d. weight and height.

_____ **14.** Changes in forms of energy are called
    a. conversions.   c. turbines.
    b. engines.   d. conservations.

_____ **15.** The maximum potential energy of a box sliding from the top of a ramp to the bottom is
    a. at the bottom of the ramp.
    b. at the top of the ramp.
    c. in the middle of the ramp.
    d. in the box itself, at all times.

_____ **16.** The maximum kinetic energy of a box sliding from the top of a ramp to the bottom is
    a. at the bottom of the ramp.
    b. at the top of the ramp.
    c. in the middle of the ramp.
    d. in the box itself, at all times.

_____ **17.** The maximum gravitational potential energy of a ball thrown up into the air is reached
    a. when it leaves the thrower's hands.
    b. as it speeds up.
    c. at the top of its path.
    d. at the bottom of its path.

_____ **18.** Zero kinetic energy occurs when
    a. velocity increases.
    b. velocity is constant but mass doubles.
    c. velocity reaches zero.
    d. a moving object falls to the Earth.

_____ **19.** An example of potential energy is
    a. energy available from fuel.
    b. an object held above the Earth's surface.
    c. a stretched spring.
    d. all of these

_____ **20.** The sun's energy as used by green plants is an example of
    a. light energy converted to kinetic energy.
    b. light energy converted to heat energy.
    c. light energy converted to mechanical energy.
    d. light energy converted to chemical energy.

_____ **21.** During nuclear fusion,
    a. there is a gain in both energy and mass.
    b. there is a loss in both energy and mass.
    c. a loss in mass produces a large gain in energy.
    d. mass is gained but energy remains constant.

_____ **22.** Energy is measured in
    a. newtons.   c. watts.
    b. meters.   d. joules.

_____ **23.** Energy associated with motion is called
    a. mechanical energy.   c. electromagnetic energy.
    b. chemical energy.   d. heat energy.

_____ **24.** The internal motion of particles of matter is called
    a. mechanical energy.   c. electromagnetic energy.
    b. chemical energy.   d. heat energy.

_____ **25.** Moving electric charges produce
    a. mechanical energy.   c. electromagnetic energy.
    b. chemical energy.   d. heat energy.

_____ **26.** An example of kinetic energy continuously being changed to potential energy and back might be
    a. a girl jumping on a trampoline.
    b. a rock poised on the top of a mountain.
    c. a moving train.
    d. electric charges moving in a straight path.

_____ **27.** Which of the following is *not* an example of mechanical energy?
    a. automobile traveling at 50 km/hr
    b. jet plane flying at 750 km/hr
    c. water in a waterfall
    d. atomic bomb exploding

_____ **28.** Which of the following has the most kinetic energy?
    a. downhill skier
    b. cross-country skier
    c. battleship moving at 50 km/hr
    d. bird flying at 50 km/hr

_____ **29.** Energy conversions occur with
    a. no loss or gain of energy.
    b. very little loss or gain of energy.
    c. energy loss due to heat.
    d. no friction.

_____ **30.** Einstein explained that
    a. mass is the same no matter where it is.
    b. mass and energy are related and can be converted into each other.
    c. mass and energy are unrelated and cannot be converted into each other.
    d. the speed of light depends on mass.

TRUE OR FALSE

Determine whether each statement is true or false.

_____ **31.** The units that measure energy are the same as the units that measure work.

_____ **32.** Mechanical energy is associated with the motion of objects.

_____ **33.** The release of nuclear energy is demonstrated by the growth of body cells.

_____ **34.** Energy of position is kinetic energy.

_____ **35.** Kinetic energy is proportional to both mass and velocity.

_____ **36.** You have potential energy when you stand still on top of a ramp.

_____ **37.** Moving electric charges have chemical energy.

_____ **38.** Kinetic and potential energies of a moving pendulum are constantly being converted into each other.

_____ **39.** As gravitational potential energy is changed to kinetic energy, there is a loss of energy.

_____ **40.** X-rays are a form of chemical energy.

COMPLETION

Fill in the word or number that best completes each statement.

_____ **41.** The ability to cause change is one of the definitions of _____.

_____ **42.** Different forms of energy are mechanical, heat, chemical, nuclear, and _____.

_____ **43.** Energy of position is called _____ energy.

_____ **44.** Energy of motion is called _____ energy.

_____ **45.** The energy in a stretched rubber band is stored, or _____.

_____ **46.** As a stretched rubber band is released, its stored energy changes to _____ energy.

_____ **47.** The energy of a moving object is called _____ energy.

_____ **48.** Objects with velocity have _____ energy.

_____ **49.** Gravitational potential energy is dependent on weight and _____.

_____ **50.** When a moving object comes to rest, its kinetic energy equals _____.

_____ **51.** Energy that is dependent on height above the Earth's surface is called _____ energy.

_____ **52.** The law of conservation of energy states that under ordinary circumstances, energy can be neither created nor _____.

_____ **53.** Light is a form of _____ energy.

_____ **54.** _____ are changes from one form of energy to another.

_____ **55.** In a motor, electromagnetic energy is converted to _____ energy.

_____ **56.** According to Einstein, _____ and energy are directly related.

_____ **57.** The unit used to measure energy is _____.

_____ **58.** The center of an atom is the source of _____ energy.

_____ **59.** _____ energy results from friction.

_____ **60.** In the process of fusion, a small loss in mass produces a large amount of _____.

Use the skills you have developed in the chapter to answer each question.

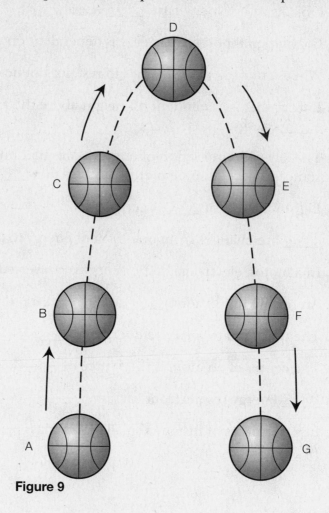

Figure 9

61. What happens in Figure 9 as the ball moves from D to G?

62. What letter in Figure 9 represents the greatest gravitational potential energy?

63. At what location in Figure 9 is kinetic energy at its maximum?

64. At what locations in Figure 9 are gravitational potential energy at a minimum?

65. At what location in Figure 9 is kinetic energy at a minimum?

66. At what point or points in Figure 9 do both kinetic and potential energies simultaneously have values other than zero? Explain your answer.

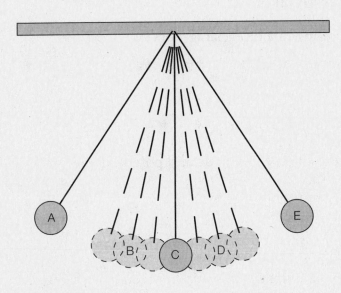

Figure 10

67. According to Figure 10, what letters represent the points of maximum gravitational potential energy?

68. At which point or points in Figure 10 would gravitational potential energy be exactly equal to kinetic energy? Explain your answer.

69. At which two points in Figure 10 is velocity equal to zero?

70. Does g, or acceleration due to gravity, change at any point in Figure 10? Explain your answer.

71. Where is the maximum kinetic energy in Figure 10?

CRITICAL THINKING AND APPLICATION

Discuss each of the following in a brief paragraph.

72. List and describe the five main forms of energy.

73. Describe the difference between kinetic and potential energy. Give an example of each.

74. How did Einstein explain the relationship between mass and energy?

75. Describe the conversions of energy that occur when a football player kicks a football, sending the ball to the opposite side of the field.

76. Describe two energy conversions that can occur during the operation of an automobile.

77. Explain the following statement: "Energy can always be converted to a different form, but it is never lost."

78. Find the potential energy and the amount of work done in lifting a 10-kg object vertically 3 m above the Earth's surface.

79. Identify the amount and kind of energy in a 6-kg object traveling at 4.0 m/sec.

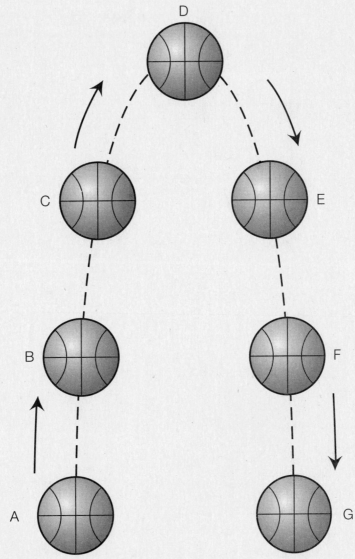

Figure 9

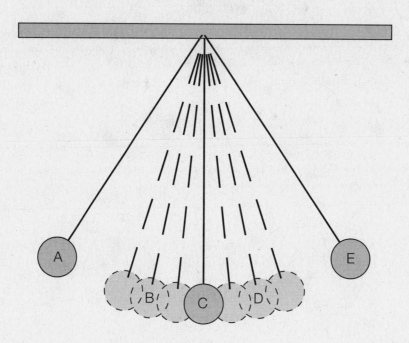

Figure 10

Test Bank Answer Key

MULTIPLE CHOICE

1. d	15. b	29. a
2. b	16. a	30. b
3. a	17. c	31. T
4. b	18. c	32. T
5. a	19. d	33. F
6. c	20. d	34. F
7. d	21. c	35. T
8. b	22. d	36. T
9. d	23. a	37. F
10. c	24. d	38. T
11. a	25. c	39. F
12. c	26. a	40. F
13. d	27. d	
14. a	28. c	

41. energy
42. electromagnetic
43. potential
44. kinetic
45. potential
46. kinetic
47. kinetic
48. kinetic
49. height
50. zero
51. gravitational potential
52. destroyed
53. electromagnetic
54. Energy conversions
55. mechanical
56. matter
57. joule
58. nuclear
59. Heat
60. energy
61. Potential energy is converted into kinetic energy.
62. D
63. G
64. A and G
65. D
66. B, C, E, and F. B and C: velocity and K.E. decrease, height and G.P.E. increase. E and F: velocity and K.E. increase, height and G.P.E. decrease. At all times, the sum of the two energies is the same.
67. A and E
68. B and D, which are halfway between maximum G.P.E. and maximum K.E. One-half of the total energy is G.P.E. and the other half is K.E.
69. At A and E, velocity equals zero.

70. No. The acceleration due to gravity, g, is constant (9.8 m/sec/sec near the surface of the Earth).
71. C
72. Mechanical energy is the energy associated with motion. Heat energy is produced by the internal motion of atoms. Chemical energy is the energy that bonds atoms together. Electromagnetic energy is produced by moving electric charges. Nuclear energy is produced by changes in the nucleus of an atom.
73. Kinetic energy is the energy an object has because of its motion. Potential energy is the stored energy an object has because of its position. Accept all logical examples.
74. Einstein viewed mass and energy as two forms of the same thing. As they change into each other, the total amount of mass and energy is conserved.
75. The football player uses mechanical energy on the football. As the players kicks the football, kinetic energy is transferred from the player's leg to the football. As the ball goes up into the air, its kinetic energy changes into gravitational potential energy. As the ball reaches the top of its path, it has its maximum G.P.E. and a K.E. value of zero. Maximum K.E. is reached when the ball hits the ground, releasing both sound and heat energy.
76. Accept all logical examples.
77. Energy is constantly converted from one form to another, such as electric energy to heat energy in a hair dryer. However, due to the law of conservation of energy, no energy is lost or gained during such energy conversions.
78. 294 J. (1) Work done is stored as gravitational potential energy in the mass. (2) W = G.P.E. = mgh = 10 kg × 9.8 m/sec/sec × 3 m = 294 J.
79. 48 J. K.E. = ½ mv = ½ 6 × 4 = ½ 96 = 48 J.

Contents

Performance-Based Assessment Rubrics

The Performance-Based Tests that follow provide you with an opportunity to evaluate both process skills and student understanding. Unlike methods of assessment that test factual recall, Performance-Based Tests demonstrate students' ability to *think logically*, utilize their *knowledge base*, *organize* their thoughts, and *perform basic skills* inherent to science and everyday life. Because students are not being tested on factual recall, it is important to keep in mind when scoring Performance-Based Tests that a logical and well-thought out answer can be scored just as high as the scientifically "correct" answer. Additional information on the theory behind performance-based assessment, as well as other forms of assessment such as portfolio assessment and oral reports, can be found on pages 76-77 in your Teacher's Desk Reference.

All of the Performance-Based Tests in the Prentice-Hall Science Learning System include one or more assessment objectives among the Teacher's Notes for each test. Using these objectives as the basis for evaluating skill development, the following assessment rubrics have been developed to assist you in your scoring. The rubrics allow for a range of student responses.

■ OUTSTANDING: RATING = 5

Student gives complete responses to all questions; provides a logical explanation for each response; completes all diagrams or data tables; uses descriptive terms accurately; completes the task; and demonstrates an understanding of the basic objectives.

■ COMPETENT: RATING = 4

Student gives complete responses to most questions, but is unable to provide a logical rationale for some answers; completes most diagrams or data tables; uses descriptive terms accurately; and demonstrates an understanding of the basic objectives.

■ SATISFACTORY: RATING = 3

Student gives incomplete answers to some questions and has a vague or limited rationale for answers; does not complete all diagrams or data tables; uses descriptive terms, but not always clearly or accurately; and demonstrates only a general understanding of the basic objectives.

■ UNSATISFACTORY: RATING = 2

Student provides very little response to most questions without any logical rationale for answers; does not complete most diagrams or data tables; does not use descriptive language; and does not exhibit an understanding of the basic objectives.

■ NO ATTEMPT: RATING = 1

Performance-Based Test

Test 1 Marble Motion

You are trying to explain motion to your friend who cannot see. The simplest things you can find are your ruler and a marble.

Check the things in front of you to make sure you have

1. metric ruler
2. marble
3. stopwatch (check that it is set at 00.00)
4. clock with a second hand
5. 2 blocks

Now you are ready to start.

1. Place the ruler flat on the table so that the groove in the ruler is on top.
2. Put the marble on top of the ruler at one end and roll the marble along the ruler.
3. The marble has moved. Write a short paragraph that describes the change in position of the marble to your friend who couldn't see the marble move.

_____

_____

_____

_____

_____

_____

4. Why did the marble move?

_____

_____

_____

5. Leave the ruler in the same position, but make the marble roll more quickly.

Motion, Forces, and Energy   S ■ 119

6. How did you do this? _____

_____

_____

_____

_____

7. What increased? _____

_____

8. What decreased? _____

_____

9. If you want to know how fast the marble is going, what would you have to measure?

_____

_____

_____

10. Place the ruler so that one end is supported by a block, making a slope. Practice letting the marble roll down the slope.

11. When you are comfortable with the marble's motion, choose the most suitable timing device to find out how long it takes the marble to roll down the slope.

12. Finally, calculate the average speed of the marble.

_____

_____

_____

_____

DID YOU KNOW?

The highest average race speed of a downhill skier is 107 kilometers per hour. This speed was achieved by Harti Weirather of Austria in the world championships of 1982.

Performance-Based Test 1: Marble Motion
Teacher Notes

MATERIALS

plastic or wooden ruler with a central channel
marble
stopwatch
clock with second hand
2 blocks of equal thickness (no more than 1 cm each)
small barrier (to prevent the marble from rolling away)

PREPARATION

Roll the marble along the ruler to make sure that it runs easily. Check that the stopwatch reads 00.00.

OBJECTIVE

This task concerns frames of reference and average speed. The students' ability to observe and draw inferences from these observations is being assessed. They also are being assessed on their ability to select the most suitable equipment for a given task.

REFERENCE

Chapter 1, What Is Motion?

Performance-Based Test

Test 2 Toy Tester

You are toy tester for a toy manufacturing company. The buyers are a little worried that the vehicle your company is selling is too fast for small children. You are going to find out how fast this small electric vehicle goes.

Check the things in front of you to make sure you have

1. vehicle (turn it on to check that it runs)
2. stopwatch (check that it reads 00.00)
3. graph paper
4. straight edge

Now you are ready to start.

1. You are going to time the vehicle over four or more distances. Prepare a data table in the space provided on this sheet. You will need to record both time and distance.

2. Using the stopwatch, find out how long it takes the vehicle to go 20 cm and record the results in your data table.
3. Repeat step 2 for 40, 60, 80, 100-cm distances.
4. Using your results, draw a graph on the graph paper provided.

5. Connect the points on your graph. What shape is the line?

_____

_____

_____

What does this tell you about the motion of the vehicle?

_____

6. According to your graph, how far does the vehicle travel in 2.5 seconds?

_____

7. What is the average speed of the vehicle? _____

DID YOU KNOW?

A Gentoo penguin can swim about 23 kilometers per hour. That's as fast as some birds fly.

Performance-Based Test 2: Toy Tester
Teacher Notes

MATERIALS

small battery-driven car or truck
tape measure or meter stick
stopwatch
graph paper
straight edge

PREPARATION

This task will need a space one-and-a-half meters long. Lay the tape measure across the space and affix it to the surface. (A tape measure is better than a long ruler because it interferes less with the task, and is longer.)

Place the stopwatch, car, straight edge, and graph paper on the surface. Make sure that the batteries are placed correctly in the vehicle.

Then turn the vehicle on to make sure it is functioning correctly. Set the stop watch to read 00.00.

OBJECTIVE

The task is concerned with constant velocity and its measurement. The students' ability to collect and present data, transfer this data to a graph, and obtain information from the resulting graph is being assessed.

REFERENCE

Chapter 1, What Is Motion?

Performance-Based Test

Test 3 Obstacle Race

You have been asked to come up with a new kind of obstacle race for the school's "spirit day." You remember that you once saw a balloon floating above an air vent and wonder if you could do something similar.

Check the things in front of you to make sure you have

1. hair dryer
2. Ping-Pong ball
3. 2 balloons suspended from 2 stands and a cross-bar

Now you are ready to start.

(You can use diagrams whenever they help with your explanation.) Looking at the things in front of you, try copying "the balloon above the air vent" idea. (Don't use the balloons; they're for later.)

What have you done? Describe what you see happening as carefully as possible.

_____

_____

_____

_____

_____

_____

You are thinking of using this idea for a race. Develop some tests to see if the idea is suitable. After you have tried the tests out, describe them.

_____

_____

_____

_____

_____

Motion, Forces, and Energy   S ■ 127

Now move the dryer out of the way and carefully move the balloons and their stands in front of you. Blow gently between the 2 balloons. What happens?

_____

_____

_____

_____

_____

Why do you think this happens? Has it any connection to the things you were doing with the hair dryer?

_____

_____

_____

_____

_____

_____

_____

Have you ever walked down a city street, turned a corner and been nearly blown off your feet by the wind? When architects design tall buildings, they must be very careful not to cause high winds between buildings. What do you think could be the cause of these high winds?

_____

_____

_____

_____

_____

_____

_____

Perhaps you have an idea about how this problem could be avoided. Describe your solution on the lines below. Maybe you'll be a great architect one day.

_____

_____

_____

_____

_____

_____

_____

_____

DID YOU KNOW?

The highest surface wind speed (371 kilometers per hour) was measured at 1916 meters on Mt. Washington, New Hampshire, on April 12, 1934. Wind in a tornado at Wichita Falls, Texas, was traveling at 450 kilometers per hour on April 2, 1958.

Performance-Based Test 3: Obstacle Race
Teacher Notes

MATERIALS

hair dryer
Ping-Pong ball
2 round balloons inflated to the same size
string (fine)
2 stands and a cross-bar
2 meter electrical extension cord

PREPARATION

Choose a hair dryer that will blow cold air. Check that the dryer is working, and then switch it on to maximum on the cold setting. Place the ball in the air stream to check that the flow is strong enough to support the ball.

Blow up the balloons to equal sizes and tie one-half meter of string to each. Suspend the balloons from the cross-bar so that there are about 10 cm between them. The cross-bar should be held in place by clamps on the lab stands.

Place the balloons at the back of the work area, and the ball and hair dryer at the front. Connect the hair dryer to a small extension cord to give the student greater flexibility.

OBJECTIVE

The students will investigate the pressure difference between still and moving air in two different ways. The students' ability to use the experience gained in a completely new context will be assessed.

REFERENCE

Chapter 3, Forces in Fluids

Performance-Based Test

Test 4 Alternative Energy Sources

Energy is currently an extremely important topic. It seems that whatever magazine you pick up, there's an article on alternative energy sources, or alternative fuels. The objects in front of you will help you explore some of these ideas.

Check the things in front of you to make sure that you have

1. propeller
2. 2 candles and holders
3. lump of clay
4. a long skewer or needle with a point on top
5. something to light the candles with

Now you are ready to start.

Look at the items in front of you. What types of energy do you speculate could be explored by using these things?

_____

_____

_____

_____

_____

_____

_____

_____

Take one of the candles and light it. What types of energy can you identify?

_____

_____

_____

_____

_____

Make sure that the propeller is balanced on the top of its support. Light the other candle and place the candles under the propeller. What do you see happening?

_____

_____

_____

_____

Trace and explain each energy conversion.

_____

_____

_____

_____

_____

_____

_____

_____

_____

Why do you think the propeller moves as it does?

_____

_____

_____

_____

_____

_____

_____

Let your imagination go a little wild. Design a machine that could work using this kind of setup.

_____

_____

_____

_____

_____

_____

_____

_____

_____

_____

_____

_____

_____

_____

_____

DID YOU KNOW?

Fire has been used as a source of energy since about 500,000 BC. The first windmills were probably built by the Persians (now called Iranians) in AD 600's.

Performance-Based Test 4: Alternative Energy Sources
Teacher Notes

MATERIALS

2 candles
2 candle holders
a disk propeller or double layer of foil, 15 cm × 15 cm
a long needle (20 cm) or a kebab skewer
support for the needle (a lump of clay will do)
a means of lighting the candle

PREPARATION

Put the propeller support in the clay so that it stands vertically. If you are using a multi-bladed propeller, set the propeller on top of the support (needle or skewer) and make sure that it spins freely. Place the candles under the propeller opposite each other (see diagram).

When you have all the equipment set up as in the diagram, light the candles to make sure that the propeller rotates.

OBJECTIVE

The students will be looking at energy conversions, and using their understanding of fluid flow and density to explain the rotation of the propeller.

REFERENCES

Chapter 3, Forces in Fluids
Chapter 5, Energy: Forms and Changes

Performance-Based Test

Test 5 Slope and Speed

Going down a very steep hill in your family's car, you saw a special run-off area for cars and trucks that lose their brakes. You have an argument with your elder sibling about the length of the area because you feel that the length and the barrier at the end are not adequate for large vehicles. Your sibling says that size makes no difference; it depends on the steepness of the hill. You are going to design an experiment to prove that you are right.

Check the things in front of you to make sure you have

1. toy car (free running)
2. larger toy car or truck
3. 5 books or thin (1.5–2.0 cm) blocks, each of the same thickness
4. flat movable surface about 1 m long, which will form a ramp
5. lightweight barrier
6. stopwatch (check that it reads 00.00)
7. metric ruler
8. spring balance (set it to 0.00)
9. pan balance
10. graph paper

Now you are ready to start.

Find out the weights and masses of the vehicles and write them down. If you draw a data table now, you can collect measurements as you go along. You may wish to use these results in supporting your argument.

Using the things that have been provided, experiment with the speed of the vehicles down different steepnesses of slopes. Don't forget to take as many measurements as you can or think you could use. Explain what you are trying to do and provide a diagram to help with your explanation.

_____

_____

_____

_____

_____

_____

_____

_____

_____

Having experimented with both vehicles and many hills, what are your conclusions about the speed the vehicles travel?

_____

_____

_____

_____

_____

Use the barrier provided to study the work the vehicles do after rolling down different slopes.

_____

_____

_____

_____

_____

_____

_____

_____

_____

_____

From the measurements you have taken you can look at the potential energy the vehicles have, their kinetic energy, and the momentum of each vehicle for each slope. Choose one of these to present as a graph showing that one vehicle possesses more of your chosen quantity than the other.

Describe the relationship you have discovered between kinetic and potential energy and momentum.

_____

_____

_____

_____

_____

_____

_____

_____

_____

_____

Which of your results are you going to use to prove to your sibling that you are correct?

_____

_____

_____

_____

_____

_____

_____

What other safety measure could be taken to improve the escape run-off?

_____

_____

_____

DID YOU KNOW?

A 50 kg person traveling in a car going 80 km/h could go through the windshield with a momentum of 4000 kg-km/h if the car stopped suddenly. A baseball would have to be traveling at 25,000 km/h to have the same momentum.

Performance-Based Test 5: Slope and Speed
Teacher Notes

MATERIALS

toy car (free running)
larger toy car or truck
5 books or thin (1.5–2.0 cm) blocks, each of the same thickness
flat movable surface about 1 m long, which will form a ramp
lightweight barrier
stopwatch
metric ruler
spring balance
pan balance
graph paper

PREPARATION

Prop one end of the surface on one book/block and make sure that both cars run down it freely. Place the barrier at the base of the ramp and run the smaller vehicle down the ramp into it. The barrier must move a measurable amount when this happens.

Check that the stopwatch is working properly and then set it to zero.

Place the books/blocks in a pile with the ramp separate from them.

OBJECTIVE

In this task the students will examine momentum and potential and kinetic energies. They will be encouraged to discover the underlying relationships between these concepts.

REFERENCES

Chapter 1, What Is Motion?
Chapter 4, Work, Power, and Simple Machines
Chapter 5, Energy: Forms and Changes